Be as a bird perched on
a frail branch that she
feels bending beneath
her, still she sings away
all the same, knowing
she has wings.

- Victor Hugo

Send all inquires to: books@mihpublishing.com

Make it Happen Publishing Inc.

ISBN: 978-1-989116-44-9

Birder's Journal
Make it Happen Publishing Inc.

This Life List Belongs to

_____

BIRDER'S LIFE LIST CONTENTS

LIST	BIRD / SPECIES	DATE SEEN	PAGE
1			
2			
3			
4			
5			
6			
7			
8			
9			
10			
11			
12			
13			
14			
15			
16			
17			
18			
19			
20			
21			
22			
23			
24			
25			
26			
27			
28			
29			
30			
31			
32			
33			
34			
35			
36			

BIRDER'S LIFE LIST CONTENTS

LIST	BIRD / SPECIES	DATE SEEN	PAGE
37			
38			
39			
40			
41			
42			
43			
44			
45			
46			
47			
48			
49			
50			
51			
52			
53			
54			
55			
56			
57			
58			
59			
60			
61			
62			
63			
64			
65			
66			
67			
68			
69			
70			
71			
72			

BIRDER'S LIFE LIST CONTENTS

LIST	BIRD / SPECIES	DATE SEEN	PAGE
73			
74			
75			
76			
77			
78			
79			
80			
81			
82			
83			
84			
85			
86			
87			
88			
89			
90			
91			
92			
93			
94			
95			
96			
97			
98			
99			
100			

Southeastern Arizona, Arizona
(Elegant Trogan, Painted Redstart, Gray Hawk, Mexican Jay, Hummigbirds)

Cape May, New Jersey
(Hawks, Warblers, Shorebirds, Waterfowls, Swallows, Wrens, Sparrows, Buntings)

J.N. "Ding" Darling National Wildlife Refuge, Florida
(Mangrove Cuckoos, Roseate Spoonbills, Wood Storks, White Ibis, Ducks, Songbirds)

Everglades National Park, Florida
(Limpkins, Snail Kites, Short-tailed Hawks, Mangrove Cuckoos, Grater Flamingos)

Corkscrew Swamp Sanctuary, Florida
(Wood Storks, Swallow-tailed Kites, Red-shouldered Hawks, Songbirds, Waders)

Point Pelee National Park, Ontario
(Over 200 speices of Songbirds, Shorebirds, Warblers)

Point Reyes National Seashore, California
(Over 200 speices of Songbirds, Shorebirds, Warblers)

Bosque del Apache National Wildlife Refuge, New Mexico
(Lesser Snow Goose, Ross's Goose, Sandhill Crane, Gambel's Quail)

Crane Creek State Park, Magee Marsh Wildlife Area, Ottawa National Wildlife Refuge, Ohio
(Tundra and Trumpeter Swan, Green Heron, Shorebirds, Warblers, Sparrows)

Monterey Bay, California
(Black-footed and Laysan Albatross, Anna's Hummingbird, Wandering Tattler)

Santa Ana National Wildlife Refuge, Texas
(Plain Chachalaca, Hook-billed Kite, Gray Hawk, Clay-colored Robin, Songbirds, Whistling-ducks, Mexican vagrants)

Big Bend National Park, Texas
(Colima Warbler, Montezuma Quail, Common Black-Hawk, and 450 more species)

Hawk Mountain Sanctuary, Pennsylvania
(Hawks, Falcons, Kestrels, Eagles, Passerines)

Jamaica Bay Wildlife Refuge, New York
(Snow Goose, Brant, Eurasian Wigeon, Tricolored Heron, Osprey, Clapper Rail, Owls, Shorebirds, and Warblers)

My Favorite Birding Locations:

1 _____
2 _____
3 _____
4 _____
5 _____
6 _____
7 _____
8 _____
9 _____
10 _____
11 _____
12 _____
13 _____
14 _____
15 _____
16 _____
17 _____
18 _____
19 _____
20 _____
21 _____
22 _____
23 _____
24 _____
25 _____
26 _____
27 _____
28 _____
29 _____
30 _____

SKETCH OR ATTACH A PHOTO OF ANY SPECIES SPECIFIC DETAILS (Image of the bird, anatomy, size, feathers etc.)

Scientific Name of Bird/Species _____
Family Name: _____

HABITAT

Observation Date: _____

Time/Duration: _____

Location: _____

Distance: _____

Weather: _____

Number Seen: _____ Male(s) _____ Female(s)

Sounds: _____

Party Size: _____

Other species also spotted in the area:

BEHAVIOR

- _____
- _____
- _____
- _____
- _____

Observation Type:
Traveling   Stationary   Historical   Incidental   Other
☐   ☐   ☐   ☐   ☐

Birding Observations/Extra Notes
Describe any important information about the bird or species

SKETCH OR ATTACH A PHOTO OF ANY SPECIES SPECIFIC DETAILS (Image of the bird, anatomy, size, feathers etc.)

Scientific Name of Bird/Species _____

Family Name: _____

Observation Date: _____

Time/Duration: _____

Location: _____

Distance: _____

Weather: _____

Number Seen: _____ Male(s) _____ Female(s)

Sounds: _____

Party Size: _____

Other species also spotted in the area:

- _____

- _____

- _____

- _____

- _____

Observation Type:

Traveling Stationary Historical Incidental Other
   ☐   ☐   ☐   ☐   ☐

HABITAT

BEHAVIOR

Birding Observations/Extra Notes

Describe any important information about the bird or species

_____
_____
_____
_____
_____
_____
_____
_____
_____
_____
_____
_____
_____
_____
_____
_____
_____
_____
_____
_____
_____
_____
_____
_____
_____
_____
_____
_____
_____

COMMON NAME OF BIRD / SPECIES

SKETCH OR ATTACH A PHOTO OF ANY SPECIES SPECIFIC DETAILS (Image of the bird, anatomy, size, feathers etc.)

Scientific Name of Bird/Species _____

Family Name: _____

Observation Date: _____

Time/Duration: _____

Location: _____

Distance: _____

Weather: _____

Number Seen: _____ Male(s) _____ Female(s)

Sounds: _____

Party Size: _____

Other species also spotted in the area:

- _____

- _____

- _____

- _____

- _____

Observation Type:

Traveling ☐ Stationary ☐ Historical ☐ Incidental ☐ Other ☐

HABITAT

BEHAVIOR

Birding Observations/Extra Notes

Describe any important information about the bird or species

_____
_____
_____
_____
_____
_____
_____
_____
_____
_____
_____
_____
_____
_____
_____
_____
_____
_____
_____
_____
_____
_____
_____
_____
_____
_____
_____
_____
_____
_____

SKETCH OR ATTACH A PHOTO OF ANY SPECIES SPECIFIC DETAILS (Image of the bird, anatomy, size, feathers etc.)

Scientific Name of Bird/Species _____

Family Name: _____

Observation Date: _____

Time/Duration: _____

Location: _____

Distance: _____

Weather: _____

Number Seen: _____ Male(s) _____ Female(s)

Sounds: _____

Party Size: _____

Other species also spotted in the area:

- _____
- _____
- _____
- _____
- _____

HABITAT

BEHAVIOR

Observation Type:

Traveling ☐ Stationary ☐ Historical ☐ Incidental ☐ Other ☐

Birding Observations/Extra Notes

Describe any important information about the bird or species

COMMON NAME OF BIRD / SPECIES

SKETCH OR ATTACH A PHOTO OF ANY SPECIES SPECIFIC DETAILS (Image of the bird, anatomy, size, feathers etc.)

Scientific Name of Bird/Species _____

Family Name: _____

Observation Date: _____

Time/Duration: _____

Location: _____

Distance: _____

Weather: _____

Number Seen: _____ Male(s) _____ Female(s)

Sounds: _____

Party Size: _____

Other species also spotted in the area:

- _____

- _____

- _____

- _____

- _____

Observation Type:

Traveling ☐   Stationary ☐   Historical ☐   Incidental ☐   Other ☐

HABITAT

BEHAVIOR

Birding Observations/Extra Notes
Describe any important information about the bird or species

SKETCH OR ATTACH A PHOTO OF ANY SPECIES SPECIFIC DETAILS (Image of the bird, anatomy, size, feathers etc.)

Scientific Name of Bird/Species _____

Family Name: _____

Observation Date: _____

Time/Duration: _____

Location: _____

Distance: _____

Weather: _____

Number Seen: ____ Male(s) ____ Female(s)

Sounds: _____

Party Size: _____

Other species also spotted in the area:

- _____
- _____
- _____
- _____
- _____

HABITAT

BEHAVIOR

Observation Type:

Traveling   Stationary   Historical   Incidental   Other
   ☐   ☐   ☐   ☐   ☐

Birding Observations/Extra Notes
Describe any important information about the bird or species

SKETCH OR ATTACH A PHOTO OF ANY SPECIES SPECIFIC DETAILS (Image of the bird, anatomy, size, feathers etc.)

Scientific Name of Bird/Species _____

Family Name: _____

Observation Date: _____

Time/Duration: _____

Location: _____

Distance: _____

Weather: _____

Number Seen: _____ Male(s) _____ Female(s)

Sounds: _____

Party Size: _____

Other species also spotted in the area:

- _____
- _____
- _____
- _____
- _____

Observation Type:

Traveling   Stationary   Historical   Incidental   Other
☐   ☐   ☐   ☐   ☐

HABITAT

BEHAVIOR

Birding Observations/Extra Notes

Describe any important information about the bird or species

_____

_____

_____

_____

_____

_____

_____

_____

_____

_____

_____

_____

_____

_____

_____

_____

_____

_____

_____

_____

_____

_____

_____

_____

_____

_____

_____

_____

_____

_____

_____

_____

SKETCH OR ATTACH A PHOTO OF ANY SPECIES SPECIFIC DETAILS (Image of the bird, anatomy, size, feathers etc.)

Scientific Name of Bird/Species _____
Family Name: _____   HABITAT
Observation Date: _____
Time/Duration: _____
Location: _____
Distance: _____
Weather: _____
Number Seen: _____ Male(s) _____ Female(s)
Sounds: _____
Party Size: _____   BEHAVIOR
Other species also spotted in the area:
- _____
- _____
- _____
- _____
- _____

Observation Type:
Traveling ☐   Stationary ☐   Historical ☐   Incidental ☐   Other ☐

Birding Observations/Extra Notes
Describe any important information about the bird or species

9 | Field Guide Notes for the _____

SKETCH OR ATTACH A PHOTO OF ANY SPECIES SPECIFIC DETAILS (Image of the bird, anatomy, size, feathers etc.)

Scientific Name of Bird/Species _____

Family Name: _____

Observation Date: _____

Time/Duration: _____

Location: _____

Distance: _____

Weather: _____

Number Seen: _____ Male(s) _____ Female(s)

Sounds: _____

Party Size: _____

Other species also spotted in the area:

- _____

- _____

- _____

- _____

- _____

HABITAT

BEHAVIOR

Observation Type:

Traveling ☐ Stationary ☐ Historical ☐ Incidental ☐ Other ☐

Birding Observations/Extra Notes
Describe any important information about the bird or species

SKETCH OR ATTACH A PHOTO OF ANY SPECIES SPECIFIC DETAILS (Image of the bird, anatomy, size, feathers etc.)

Scientific Name of Bird/Species _____

Family Name: _____

Observation Date: _____

Time/Duration: _____

Location: _____

Distance: _____

Weather: _____

Number Seen: _____ Male(s) _____ Female(s)

Sounds: _____

Party Size: _____

Other species also spotted in the area:

- _____
- _____
- _____
- _____
- _____

HABITAT

BEHAVIOR

Observation Type:

Traveling ☐ Stationary ☐ Historical ☐ Incidental ☐ Other ☐

Birding Observations/Extra Notes

Describe any important information about the bird or species

SKETCH OR ATTACH A PHOTO OF ANY SPECIES SPECIFIC DETAILS (Image of the bird, anatomy, size, feathers etc.)

Scientific Name of Bird/Species _____

Family Name: _____

Observation Date: _____

Time/Duration: _____

Location: _____

Distance: _____

Weather: _____

Number Seen: _____ Male(s) _____ Female(s)

Sounds: _____

Party Size: _____

Other species also spotted in the area:

- _____
- _____
- _____
- _____
- _____

HABITAT

BEHAVIOR

Observation Type:

Traveling ☐   Stationary ☐   Historical ☐   Incidental ☐   Other ☐

Birding Observations/Extra Notes
Describe any important information about the bird or species

SKETCH OR ATTACH A PHOTO OF ANY SPECIES SPECIFIC DETAILS (Image of the bird, anatomy, size, feathers etc.)

Scientific Name of Bird/Species _____

Family Name: _____

Observation Date: _____

Time/Duration: _____

Location: _____

Distance: _____

Weather: _____

Number Seen: _____ Male(s) _____ Female(s)

Sounds: _____

Party Size: _____

Other species also spotted in the area:

- _____
- _____
- _____
- _____
- _____

Observation Type:

Traveling ☐ Stationary ☐ Historical ☐ Incidental ☐ Other ☐

HABITAT

BEHAVIOR

Birding Observations/Extra Notes

Describe any important information about the bird or species

_____

_____

_____

_____

_____

_____

_____

_____

_____

_____

_____

_____

_____

_____

_____

_____

_____

_____

_____

_____

_____

_____

_____

_____

_____

_____

_____

_____

_____

SKETCH OR ATTACH A PHOTO OF ANY SPECIES SPECIFIC DETAILS (Image of the bird, anatomy, size, feathers etc.)

Scientific Name of Bird/Species _____

Family Name: _____

Observation Date: _____

Time/Duration: _____

Location: _____

Distance: _____

Weather: _____

Number Seen: _____ Male(s) _____ Female(s)

Sounds: _____

Party Size: _____

Other species also spotted in the area:

- _____
- _____
- _____
- _____
- _____

Observation Type:

Traveling ☐   Stationary ☐   Historical ☐   Incidental ☐   Other ☐

HABITAT

BEHAVIOR

Birding Observations/Extra Notes

Describe any important information about the bird or species

_____

_____

_____

_____

_____

_____

_____

_____

_____

_____

_____

_____

_____

_____

_____

_____

_____

_____

_____

_____

_____

_____

_____

_____

_____

_____

_____

_____

SKETCH OR ATTACH A PHOTO OF ANY SPECIES SPECIFIC DETAILS (Image of the bird, anatomy, size, feathers etc.)

Scientific Name of Bird/Species _____

Family Name: _____

Observation Date: _____

Time/Duration: _____

Location: _____

Distance: _____

Weather: _____

Number Seen: _____ Male(s) _____ Female(s)

Sounds: _____

Party Size: _____

Other species also spotted in the area:

- _____
- _____
- _____
- _____
- _____

HABITAT

BEHAVIOR

Observation Type:

Traveling ☐ Stationary ☐ Historical ☐ Incidental ☐ Other ☐

Birding Observations/Extra Notes

Describe any important information about the bird or species

SKETCH OR ATTACH A PHOTO OF ANY SPECIES SPECIFIC DETAILS (Image of the bird, anatomy, size, feathers etc.)

Scientific Name of Bird/Species _____

Family Name: _____

Observation Date: _____

Time/Duration: _____

Location: _____

Distance: _____

Weather: _____

Number Seen: _____ Male(s) _____ Female(s)

Sounds: _____

Party Size: _____

Other species also spotted in the area:

- _____
- _____
- _____
- _____
- _____

Observation Type:

Traveling ☐   Stationary ☐   Historical ☐   Incidental ☐   Other ☐

HABITAT

BEHAVIOR

Birding Observations/Extra Notes
Describe any important information about the bird or species

SKETCH OR ATTACH A PHOTO OF ANY SPECIES SPECIFIC DETAILS (Image of the bird, anatomy, size, feathers etc.)

Scientific Name of Bird/Species _____

Family Name: _____   HABITAT

Observation Date: _____

Time/Duration: _____

Location: _____

Distance: _____

Weather: _____

Number Seen: _____ Male(s) _____ Female(s)

Sounds: _____

Party Size: _____

Other species also spotted in the area: BEHAVIOR

- _____
- _____
- _____
- _____
- _____

Observation Type:

Traveling Stationary Historical Incidental Other
  ☐   ☐   ☐   ☐   ☐

Birding Observations/Extra Notes

Describe any important information about the bird or species

SKETCH OR ATTACH A PHOTO OF ANY SPECIES SPECIFIC DETAILS (Image of the bird, anatomy, size, feathers etc.)

Scientific Name of Bird/Species _____

Family Name: _____

Observation Date: _____

Time/Duration: _____

Location: _____

Distance: _____

Weather: _____

Number Seen: _____ Male(s) _____ Female(s)

Sounds: _____

Party Size: _____

Other species also spotted in the area:

- _____
- _____
- _____
- _____
- _____

Observation Type:

Traveling ☐ Stationary ☐ Historical ☐ Incidental ☐ Other ☐

HABITAT

BEHAVIOR

Birding Observations/Extra Notes
Describe any important information about the bird or species

18 | Field Guide Notes for the _____

COMMON NAME OF BIRD / SPECIES

SKETCH OR ATTACH A PHOTO OF ANY SPECIES SPECIFIC DETAILS (Image of the bird, anatomy, size, feathers etc.)

Scientific Name of Bird/Species _____

Family Name: _____   HABITAT

Observation Date: _____

Time/Duration: _____

Location: _____

Distance: _____

Weather: _____

Number Seen: ____ Male(s) ____ Female(s)

Sounds: _____

Party Size: _____   BEHAVIOR

Other species also spotted in the area:

- _____

- _____

- _____

- _____

- _____

Observation Type:

Traveling ☐   Stationary ☐   Historical ☐   Incidental ☐   Other ☐

Birding Observations/Extra Notes
Describe any important information about the bird or species

COMMON NAME OF BIRD / SPECIES

SKETCH OR ATTACH A PHOTO OF ANY SPECIES SPECIFIC DETAILS (Image of the bird, anatomy, size, feathers etc.)

Scientific Name of Bird/Species _____

Family Name: _____

Observation Date: _____

Time/Duration: _____

Location: _____

Distance: _____

Weather: _____

Number Seen: _____ Male(s) _____ Female(s)

Sounds: _____

Party Size: _____

Other species also spotted in the area:

- _____
- _____
- _____
- _____
- _____

Observation Type:

Traveling ☐ Stationary ☐ Historical ☐ Incidental ☐ Other ☐

HABITAT

BEHAVIOR

Birding Observations/Extra Notes
Describe any important information about the bird or species

SKETCH OR ATTACH A PHOTO OF ANY SPECIES SPECIFIC DETAILS (Image of the bird, anatomy, size, feathers etc.)

Scientific Name of Bird/Species _____

Family Name: _____

Observation Date: _____

Time/Duration: _____

Location: _____

Distance: _____

Weather: _____

Number Seen: _____ Male(s) _____ Female(s)

Sounds: _____

Party Size: _____

Other species also spotted in the area:

- _____
- _____
- _____
- _____
- _____

HABITAT

BEHAVIOR

Observation Type:

Traveling ☐ Stationary ☐ Historical ☐ Incidental ☐ Other ☐

Birding Observations/Extra Notes
Describe any important information about the bird or species

SKETCH OR ATTACH A PHOTO OF ANY SPECIES SPECIFIC DETAILS (Image of the bird, anatomy, size, feathers etc.)

Scientific Name of Bird/Species _____

Family Name: _____

Observation Date: _____

Time/Duration: _____

Location: _____

Distance: _____

Weather: _____

Number Seen: _____ Male(s) _____ Female(s)

Sounds: _____

Party Size: _____

Other species also spotted in the area:

- _____
- _____
- _____
- _____
- _____

Observation Type:

Traveling ☐   Stationary ☐   Historical ☐   Incidental ☐   Other ☐

HABITAT

BEHAVIOR

Birding Observations/Extra Notes

Describe any important information about the bird or species

SKETCH OR ATTACH A PHOTO OF ANY SPECIES SPECIFIC DETAILS (Image of the bird, anatomy, size, feathers etc.)

Scientific Name of Bird/Species _____

Family Name: _____

Observation Date: _____

Time/Duration: _____

Location: _____

Distance: _____

Weather: _____

Number Seen: _____ Male(s) _____ Female(s)

Sounds: _____

Party Size: _____

Other species also spotted in the area:

- _____

- _____

- _____

- _____

- _____

Observation Type:

Traveling ☐   Stationary ☐   Historical ☐   Incidental ☐   Other ☐

HABITAT

BEHAVIOR

Birding Observations/Extra Notes

Describe any important information about the bird or species

_____

_____

_____

_____

_____

_____

_____

_____

_____

_____

_____

_____

_____

_____

_____

_____

_____

_____

_____

_____

_____

_____

_____

_____

_____

_____

SKETCH OR ATTACH A PHOTO OF ANY SPECIES SPECIFIC DETAILS (Image of the bird, anatomy, size, feathers etc.)

Scientific Name of Bird/Species _____

Family Name: _____

Observation Date: _____

Time/Duration: _____

Location: _____

Distance: _____

Weather: _____

Number Seen: _____ Male(s) _____ Female(s)

Sounds: _____

Party Size: _____

Other species also spotted in the area:

- _____
- _____
- _____
- _____
- _____

HABITAT

BEHAVIOR

Observation Type:

Traveling ☐   Stationary ☐   Historical ☐   Incidental ☐   Other ☐

Birding Observations/Extra Notes
Describe any important information about the bird or species

SKETCH OR ATTACH A PHOTO OF ANY SPECIES SPECIFIC DETAILS (Image of the bird, anatomy, size, feathers etc.)

Scientific Name of Bird/Species _____

Family Name: _____

Observation Date: _____

Time/Duration: _____

Location: _____

Distance: _____

Weather: _____

Number Seen: _____ Male(s) _____ Female(s)

Sounds: _____

Party Size: _____

Other species also spotted in the area:

- _____
- _____
- _____
- _____
- _____

Observation Type:

Traveling ☐   Stationary ☐   Historical ☐   Incidental ☐   Other ☐

HABITAT

BEHAVIOR

Birding Observations/Extra Notes
Describe any important information about the bird or species

SKETCH OR ATTACH A PHOTO OF ANY SPECIES SPECIFIC DETAILS (Image of the bird, anatomy, size, feathers etc.)

Scientific Name of Bird/Species _____

Family Name: _____   HABITAT

Observation Date: _____

Time/Duration: _____

Location: _____

Distance: _____

Weather: _____

Number Seen: _____ Male(s) _____ Female(s)

Sounds: _____

Party Size: _____   BEHAVIOR

Other species also spotted in the area:

- _____

- _____

- _____

- _____

- _____

Observation Type:

Traveling ☐   Stationary ☐   Historical ☐   Incidental ☐   Other ☐

Birding Observations/Extra Notes
Describe any important information about the bird or species

_____

_____

_____

_____

_____

_____

_____

_____

_____

_____

_____

_____

_____

_____

_____

_____

_____

_____

_____

_____

_____

_____

_____

_____

_____

_____

_____

_____

_____

_____

SKETCH OR ATTACH A PHOTO OF ANY SPECIES SPECIFIC DETAILS (Image of the bird, anatomy, size, feathers etc.)

Scientific Name of Bird/Species _____
Family Name: _____
Observation Date: _____
Time/Duration: _____
Location: _____
Distance: _____
Weather: _____
Number Seen: _____ Male(s) _____ Female(s)
Sounds: _____
Party Size: _____
Other species also spotted in the area:
- _____
- _____
- _____
- _____
- _____

Observation Type:
Traveling ☐ Stationary ☐ Historical ☐ Incidental ☐ Other ☐

HABITAT

BEHAVIOR

Birding Observations/Extra Notes
Describe any important information about the bird or species

SKETCH OR ATTACH A PHOTO OF ANY SPECIES SPECIFIC DETAILS (Image of the bird, anatomy, size, feathers etc.)

Scientific Name of Bird/Species _____

Family Name: _____

Observation Date: _____

Time/Duration: _____

Location: _____

Distance: _____

Weather: _____

Number Seen: _____ Male(s) _____ Female(s)

Sounds: _____

Party Size: _____

Other species also spotted in the area:

- _____

- _____

- _____

- _____

- _____

HABITAT

BEHAVIOR

Observation Type:

Traveling ☐   Stationary ☐   Historical ☐   Incidental ☐   Other ☐

Birding Observations/Extra Notes
Describe any important information about the bird or species

---

28 | Field Guide Notes for the _____

COMMON NAME OF BIRD / SPECIES

SKETCH OR ATTACH A PHOTO OF ANY SPECIES SPECIFIC DETAILS (Image of the bird, anatomy, size, feathers etc.)

Scientific Name of Bird/Species _____
Family Name: _____
Observation Date: _____
Time/Duration: _____
Location: _____
Distance: _____
Weather: _____
Number Seen: _____ Male(s) _____ Female(s)
Sounds: _____
Party Size: _____
Other species also spotted in the area:
- _____
- _____
- _____
- _____
- _____

HABITAT

BEHAVIOR

Observation Type:
Traveling ☐ Stationary ☐ Historical ☐ Incidental ☐ Other ☐

Birding Observations/Extra Notes

Describe any important information about the bird or species

SKETCH OR ATTACH A PHOTO OF ANY SPECIES SPECIFIC DETAILS (Image of the bird, anatomy, size, feathers etc.)

Scientific Name of Bird/Species _____

Family Name: _____

Observation Date: _____

Time/Duration: _____

Location: _____

Distance: _____

Weather: _____

Number Seen: _____ Male(s) _____ Female(s)

Sounds: _____

Party Size: _____

Other species also spotted in the area:

- _____
- _____
- _____
- _____
- _____

HABITAT

BEHAVIOR

Observation Type:

Traveling ☐   Stationary ☐   Historical ☐   Incidental ☐   Other ☐

Birding Observations/Extra Notes

Describe any important information about the bird or species

SKETCH OR ATTACH A PHOTO OF ANY SPECIES SPECIFIC DETAILS (Image of the bird, anatomy, size, feathers etc.)

Scientific Name of Bird/Species _____

Family Name: _____

Observation Date: _____

Time/Duration: _____

Location: _____

Distance: _____

Weather: _____

Number Seen: ____ Male(s) ____ Female(s)

Sounds: _____

Party Size: _____

Other species also spotted in the area:

- _____
- _____
- _____
- _____
- _____

HABITAT

BEHAVIOR

Observation Type:

Traveling ☐ Stationary ☐ Historical ☐ Incidental ☐ Other ☐

Birding Observations/Extra Notes

Describe any important information about the bird or species

_____

_____

_____

_____

_____

_____

_____

_____

_____

_____

_____

_____

_____

_____

_____

_____

_____

_____

_____

_____

_____

_____

_____

_____

_____

_____

_____

_____

_____

_____

31 | Field Guide Notes for the _____

COMMON NAME OF BIRD / SPECIES

SKETCH OR ATTACH A PHOTO OF ANY SPECIES SPECIFIC DETAILS (Image of the bird, anatomy, size, feathers etc.)

Scientific Name of Bird/Species _____

Family Name: _____

Observation Date: _____

Time/Duration: _____

Location: _____

Distance: _____

Weather: _____

Number Seen: _____ Male(s) _____ Female(s)

Sounds: _____

Party Size: _____

Other species also spotted in the area:

- _____
- _____
- _____
- _____
- _____

Observation Type:

Traveling   Stationary   Historical   Incidental   Other
□   □   □   □   □

HABITAT

BEHAVIOR

Birding Observations/Extra Notes

Describe any important information about the bird or species

_____
_____
_____
_____
_____
_____
_____
_____
_____
_____
_____
_____
_____
_____
_____
_____
_____
_____
_____
_____
_____
_____
_____
_____
_____
_____

32 | Field Guide Notes for the _____

COMMON NAME OF BIRD / SPECIES

SKETCH OR ATTACH A PHOTO OF ANY SPECIES SPECIFIC DETAILS (Image of the bird, anatomy, size, feathers etc.)

Scientific Name of Bird/Species _____

Family Name: _____

Observation Date: _____

Time/Duration: _____

Location: _____

Distance: _____

Weather: _____

Number Seen: _____ Male(s) _____ Female(s)

Sounds: _____

Party Size: _____

Other species also spotted in the area:

- _____
- _____
- _____
- _____
- _____

Observation Type:

Traveling ☐ Stationary ☐ Historical ☐ Incidental ☐ Other ☐

HABITAT

BEHAVIOR

Birding Observations/Extra Notes
Describe any important information about the bird or species

33 | Field Guide Notes for the _____

COMMON NAME OF BIRD / SPECIES

SKETCH OR ATTACH A PHOTO OF ANY SPECIES SPECIFIC DETAILS (Image of the bird, anatomy, size, feathers etc.)

Scientific Name of Bird/Species _____

Family Name: _____

Observation Date: _____

Time/Duration: _____

Location: _____

Distance: _____

Weather: _____

Number Seen: _____ Male(s) _____ Female(s)

Sounds: _____

Party Size: _____

Other species also spotted in the area:

- _____

- _____

- _____

- _____

- _____

Observation Type:

Traveling ☐   Stationary ☐   Historical ☐   Incidental ☐   Other ☐

HABITAT

BEHAVIOR

Birding Observations/Extra Notes
Describe any important information about the bird or species

34 Field Guide Notes for the _____

COMMON NAME OF BIRD / SPECIES

SKETCH OR ATTACH A PHOTO OF ANY SPECIES SPECIFIC DETAILS (Image of the bird, anatomy, size, feathers etc.)

Scientific Name of Bird/Species _____
Family Name: _____
Observation Date: _____
Time/Duration: _____
Location: _____
Distance: _____
Weather: _____
Number Seen: ____ Male(s) ____ Female(s)
Sounds: _____
Party Size: _____
Other species also spotted in the area:
- _____
- _____
- _____
- _____
- _____

Observation Type:
Traveling   Stationary   Historical   Incidental   Other
☐   ☐   ☐   ☐   ☐

HABITAT

BEHAVIOR

Birding Observations/Extra Notes

Describe any important information about the bird or species

SKETCH OR ATTACH A PHOTO OF ANY SPECIES SPECIFIC DETAILS (Image of the bird, anatomy, size, feathers etc.)

Scientific Name of Bird/Species _____

Family Name: _____

Observation Date: _____

Time/Duration: _____

Location: _____

Distance: _____

Weather: _____

Number Seen: _____ Male(s) _____ Female(s)

Sounds: _____

Party Size: _____

Other species also spotted in the area:

- _____
- _____
- _____
- _____
- _____

HABITAT

BEHAVIOR

Observation Type:

Traveling ☐   Stationary ☐   Historical ☐   Incidental ☐   Other ☐

Birding Observations/Extra Notes

Describe any important information about the bird or species

SKETCH OR ATTACH A PHOTO OF ANY SPECIES SPECIFIC DETAILS (Image of the bird, anatomy, size, feathers etc.)

Scientific Name of Bird/Species _____

Family Name: _____

Observation Date: _____

Time/Duration: _____

Location: _____

Distance: _____

Weather: _____

Number Seen: _____ Male(s) _____ Female(s)

Sounds: _____

Party Size: _____

Other species also spotted in the area:

- _____
- _____
- _____
- _____
- _____

HABITAT

BEHAVIOR

Observation Type:

Traveling ☐   Stationary ☐   Historical ☐   Incidental ☐   Other ☐

Birding Observations/Extra Notes
Describe any important information about the bird or species

SKETCH OR ATTACH A PHOTO OF ANY SPECIES SPECIFIC DETAILS (Image of the bird, anatomy, size, feathers etc.)

Scientific Name of Bird/Species _____

Family Name: _____

Observation Date: _____

Time/Duration: _____

Location: _____

Distance: _____

Weather: _____

Number Seen: _____ Male(s) _____ Female(s)

Sounds: _____

Party Size: _____

Other species also spotted in the area:

- _____
- _____
- _____
- _____
- _____

HABITAT

BEHAVIOR

Observation Type:

Traveling ☐   Stationary ☐   Historical ☐   Incidental ☐   Other ☐

Birding Observations/Extra Notes
Describe any important information about the bird or species

SKETCH OR ATTACH A PHOTO OF ANY SPECIES SPECIFIC DETAILS (Image of the bird, anatomy, size, feathers etc.)

Scientific Name of Bird/Species _____

Family Name: _____

Observation Date: _____

Time/Duration: _____

Location: _____

Distance: _____

Weather: _____

Number Seen: _____ Male(s) _____ Female(s)

Sounds: _____

Party Size: _____

Other species also spotted in the area:

- _____
- _____
- _____
- _____
- _____

Observation Type:

Traveling ☐ Stationary ☐ Historical ☐ Incidental ☐ Other ☐

HABITAT

BEHAVIOR

Birding Observations/Extra Notes
Describe any important information about the bird or species

39 | Field Guide Notes for the _____
COMMON NAME OF BIRD / SPECIES

SKETCH OR ATTACH A PHOTO OF ANY SPECIES SPECIFIC DETAILS (Image of the bird, anatomy, size, feathers etc.)

Scientific Name of Bird/Species _____

Family Name: _____

Observation Date: _____

Time/Duration: _____

Location: _____

Distance: _____

Weather: _____

Number Seen: _____ Male(s) _____ Female(s)

Sounds: _____

Party Size: _____

Other species also spotted in the area:

- _____
- _____
- _____
- _____
- _____

Observation Type:

Traveling ☐   Stationary ☐   Historical ☐   Incidental ☐   Other ☐

HABITAT

BEHAVIOR

Birding Observations/Extra Notes
Describe any important information about the bird or species

_____

_____

_____

_____

_____

_____

_____

_____

_____

_____

_____

_____

_____

_____

_____

_____

_____

_____

_____

_____

_____

_____

_____

_____

_____

_____

_____

_____

_____

_____

SKETCH OR ATTACH A PHOTO OF ANY SPECIES SPECIFIC DETAILS (Image of the bird, anatomy, size, feathers etc.)

Scientific Name of Bird/Species _____

Family Name: _____

Observation Date: _____

Time/Duration: _____

Location: _____

Distance: _____

Weather: _____

Number Seen: _____ Male(s) _____ Female(s)

Sounds: _____

Party Size: _____

Other species also spotted in the area:

- _____
- _____
- _____
- _____
- _____

Observation Type:
Traveling   Stationary   Historical   Incidental   Other
☐   ☐   ☐   ☐   ☐

HABITAT

BEHAVIOR

Birding Observations/Extra Notes

Describe any important information about the bird or species

_____
_____
_____
_____
_____
_____
_____
_____
_____
_____
_____
_____
_____
_____
_____
_____
_____
_____
_____
_____
_____
_____
_____
_____
_____
_____
_____
_____

SKETCH OR ATTACH A PHOTO OF ANY SPECIES SPECIFIC DETAILS (Image of the bird, anatomy, size, feathers etc.)

Scientific Name of Bird/Species _____

Family Name: _____

Observation Date: _____

Time/Duration: _____

Location: _____

Distance: _____

Weather: _____

Number Seen: _____ Male(s) _____ Female(s)

Sounds: _____

Party Size: _____

Other species also spotted in the area:

- _____
- _____
- _____
- _____
- _____

Observation Type:

Traveling ☐   Stationary ☐   Historical ☐   Incidental ☐   Other ☐

HABITAT

BEHAVIOR

Birding Observations/Extra Notes

Describe any important information about the bird or species

COMMON NAME OF BIRD / SPECIES

SKETCH OR ATTACH A PHOTO OF ANY SPECIES SPECIFIC DETAILS (Image of the bird, anatomy, size, feathers etc.)

Scientific Name of Bird/Species _____
Family Name: _____   HABITAT
Observation Date: _____
Time/Duration: _____
Location: _____
Distance: _____
Weather: _____
Number Seen: ____ Male(s) ____ Female(s)
Sounds: _____
Party Size: _____
Other species also spotted in the area: BEHAVIOR

- _____
- _____
- _____
- _____
- _____

Observation Type:
Traveling ☐ Stationary ☐ Historical ☐ Incidental ☐ Other ☐

Birding Observations/Extra Notes
Describe any important information about the bird or species

SKETCH OR ATTACH A PHOTO OF ANY SPECIES SPECIFIC DETAILS (Image of the bird, anatomy, size, feathers etc.)

Scientific Name of Bird/Species _____

Family Name: _____

Observation Date: _____

Time/Duration: _____

Location: _____

Distance: _____

Weather: _____

Number Seen: _____ Male(s) _____ Female(s)

Sounds: _____

Party Size: _____

Other species also spotted in the area:

- _____

- _____

- _____

- _____

- _____

Observation Type:

Traveling   Stationary   Historical   Incidental   Other
☐   ☐   ☐   ☐   ☐

HABITAT

BEHAVIOR

Birding Observations/Extra Notes
Describe any important information about the bird or species

SKETCH OR ATTACH A PHOTO OF ANY SPECIES SPECIFIC DETAILS (Image of the bird, anatomy, size, feathers etc.)

Scientific Name of Bird/Species _____

Family Name: _____

Observation Date: _____

Time/Duration: _____

Location: _____

Distance: _____

Weather: _____

Number Seen: _____ Male(s) _____ Female(s)

Sounds: _____

Party Size: _____

Other species also spotted in the area:

- _____
- _____
- _____
- _____
- _____

Observation Type:

Traveling   Stationary   Historical   Incidental   Other
☐   ☐   ☐   ☐   ☐

HABITAT

BEHAVIOR

Birding Observations/Extra Notes

Describe any important information about the bird or species

SKETCH OR ATTACH A PHOTO OF ANY SPECIES SPECIFIC DETAILS (Image of the bird, anatomy, size, feathers etc.)

Scientific Name of Bird/Species _____

Family Name: _____

Observation Date: _____

Time/Duration: _____

Location: _____

Distance: _____

Weather: _____

Number Seen: _____ Male(s) _____ Female(s)

Sounds: _____

Party Size: _____

Other species also spotted in the area:

- _____
- _____
- _____
- _____
- _____

Observation Type:

Traveling ☐   Stationary ☐   Historical ☐   Incidental ☐   Other ☐

HABITAT

BEHAVIOR

Birding Observations/Extra Notes

Describe any important information about the bird or species

_____
_____
_____
_____
_____
_____
_____
_____
_____
_____
_____
_____
_____
_____
_____
_____
_____
_____
_____
_____
_____
_____
_____
_____
_____
_____
_____
_____

SKETCH OR ATTACH A PHOTO OF ANY SPECIES SPECIFIC DETAILS (Image of the bird, anatomy, size, feathers etc.)

Scientific Name of Bird/Species _____

Family Name: _____

Observation Date: _____

Time/Duration: _____

Location: _____

Distance: _____

Weather: _____

Number Seen: _____ Male(s) _____ Female(s)

Sounds: _____

Party Size: _____

Other species also spotted in the area:

- _____

- _____

- _____

- _____

- _____

Observation Type:

Traveling ☐   Stationary ☐   Historical ☐   Incidental ☐   Other ☐

HABITAT

BEHAVIOR

Birding Observations/Extra Notes
Describe any important information about the bird or species

SKETCH OR ATTACH A PHOTO OF ANY SPECIES SPECIFIC DETAILS (Image of the bird, anatomy, size, feathers etc.)

Scientific Name of Bird/Species _____

Family Name: _____

Observation Date: _____

Time/Duration: _____

Location: _____

Distance: _____

Weather: _____

Number Seen: _____ Male(s) _____ Female(s)

Sounds: _____

Party Size: _____

Other species also spotted in the area:

- _____
- _____
- _____
- _____
- _____

Observation Type:

Traveling ☐   Stationary ☐   Historical ☐   Incidental ☐   Other ☐

HABITAT

BEHAVIOR

Birding Observations/Extra Notes

Describe any important information about the bird or species

SKETCH OR ATTACH A PHOTO OF ANY SPECIES SPECIFIC DETAILS (Image of the bird, anatomy, size, feathers etc.)

Scientific Name of Bird/Species _____

Family Name: _____

Observation Date: _____

Time/Duration: _____

Location: _____

Distance: _____

Weather: _____

Number Seen: _____ Male(s) _____ Female(s)

Sounds: _____

Party Size: _____

Other species also spotted in the area:

- _____
- _____
- _____
- _____
- _____

Observation Type:

Traveling ☐ Stationary ☐ Historical ☐ Incidental ☐ Other ☐

HABITAT

BEHAVIOR

Birding Observations/Extra Notes

Describe any important information about the bird or species

SKETCH OR ATTACH A PHOTO OF ANY SPECIES SPECIFIC DETAILS (Image of the bird, anatomy, size, feathers etc.)

Scientific Name of Bird/Species _____

Family Name: _____

Observation Date: _____

Time/Duration: _____

Location: _____

Distance: _____

Weather: _____

Number Seen: _____ Male(s) _____ Female(s)

Sounds: _____

Party Size: _____

Other species also spotted in the area:

- _____
- _____
- _____
- _____
- _____

Observation Type:

Traveling ☐   Stationary ☐   Historical ☐   Incidental ☐   Other ☐

HABITAT

BEHAVIOR

Birding Observations/Extra Notes
Describe any important information about the bird or species

50 | Field Guide Notes for the _____

*COMMON NAME OF BIRD / SPECIES**COMMON NAME OF BIRD / SPECIES*

SKETCH OR ATTACH A PHOTO OF ANY SPECIES SPECIFIC DETAILS (Image of the bird, anatomy, size, feathers etc.)

Scientific Name of Bird/Species _____
Family Name: _____   HABITAT
Observation Date: _____
Time/Duration: _____
Location: _____
Distance: _____
Weather: _____
Number Seen: _____ Male(s) _____ Female(s)
Sounds: _____
Party Size: _____
Other species also spotted in the area: BEHAVIOR
- _____
- _____
- _____
- _____
- _____

Observation Type:
Traveling   Stationary   Historical   Incidental   Other
☐   ☐   ☐   ☐   ☐

Birding Observations/Extra Notes
Describe any important information about the bird or species

Field Guide Notes for the _____

COMMON NAME OF BIRD / SPECIES

SKETCH OR ATTACH A PHOTO OF ANY SPECIES SPECIFIC DETAILS (Image of the bird, anatomy, size, feathers etc.)

Scientific Name of Bird/Species _____

Family Name: _____

HABITAT

Observation Date: _____

Time/Duration: _____

Location: _____

Distance: _____

Weather: _____

Number Seen: _____ Male(s) _____ Female(s)

Sounds: _____

Party Size: _____

BEHAVIOR

Other species also spotted in the area:

- _____

- _____

- _____

- _____

- _____

Observation Type:

Traveling ☐ Stationary ☐ Historical ☐ Incidental ☐ Other ☐

Birding Observations/Extra Notes

Describe any important information about the bird or species

_____

_____

_____

_____

_____

_____

_____

_____

_____

_____

_____

_____

_____

_____

_____

_____

_____

_____

_____

_____

_____

_____

_____

_____

_____

_____

_____

_____

SKETCH OR ATTACH A PHOTO OF ANY SPECIES SPECIFIC DETAILS (Image of the bird, anatomy, size, feathers etc.)

Scientific Name of Bird/Species _____

Family Name: _____

Observation Date: _____

Time/Duration: _____

Location: _____

Distance: _____

Weather: _____

Number Seen: _____ Male(s) _____ Female(s)

Sounds: _____

Party Size: _____

Other species also spotted in the area:

- _____
- _____
- _____
- _____
- _____

Observation Type:

Traveling ☐   Stationary ☐   Historical ☐   Incidental ☐   Other ☐

HABITAT

BEHAVIOR

Birding Observations/Extra Notes
Describe any important information about the bird or species

SKETCH OR ATTACH A PHOTO OF ANY SPECIES SPECIFIC DETAILS (Image of the bird, anatomy, size, feathers etc.)

Scientific Name of Bird/Species _____

Family Name: _____

Observation Date: _____

Time/Duration: _____

Location: _____

Distance: _____

Weather: _____

Number Seen: _____ Male(s) _____ Female(s)

Sounds: _____

Party Size: _____

Other species also spotted in the area:

- _____
- _____
- _____
- _____
- _____

Observation Type:

Traveling ☐ Stationary ☐ Historical ☐ Incidental ☐ Other ☐

HABITAT

BEHAVIOR

Birding Observations/Extra Notes
Describe any important information about the bird or species

SKETCH OR ATTACH A PHOTO OF ANY SPECIES SPECIFIC DETAILS (Image of the bird, anatomy, size, feathers etc.)

Scientific Name of Bird/Species _____

Family Name: _____   HABITAT

Observation Date: _____

Time/Duration: _____

Location: _____

Distance: _____

Weather: _____

Number Seen: _____ Male(s) _____ Female(s)

Sounds: _____

Party Size: _____

Other species also spotted in the area: BEHAVIOR

- _____
- _____
- _____
- _____
- _____

Observation Type:

Traveling   Stationary   Historical   Incidental   Other
   ☐   ☐   ☐   ☐   ☐

Birding Observations/Extra Notes
Describe any important information about the bird or species

SKETCH OR ATTACH A PHOTO OF ANY SPECIES SPECIFIC DETAILS (Image of the bird, anatomy, size, feathers etc.)

Scientific Name of Bird/Species _____

Family Name: _____

Observation Date: _____

Time/Duration: _____

Location: _____

Distance: _____

Weather: _____

Number Seen: _____ Male(s) _____ Female(s)

Sounds: _____

Party Size: _____

Other species also spotted in the area:

- _____
- _____
- _____
- _____
- _____

Observation Type:

Traveling ☐ Stationary ☐ Historical ☐ Incidental ☐ Other ☐

HABITAT

BEHAVIOR

Birding Observations/Extra Notes
Describe any important information about the bird or species

SKETCH OR ATTACH A PHOTO OF ANY SPECIES SPECIFIC DETAILS (Image of the bird, anatomy, size, feathers etc.)

Scientific Name of Bird/Species _____

Family Name: _____

Observation Date: _____

Time/Duration: _____

Location: _____

Distance: _____

Weather: _____

Number Seen: _____ Male(s) _____ Female(s)

Sounds: _____

Party Size: _____

HABITAT

Other species also spotted in the area:

- _____
- _____
- _____
- _____
- _____

BEHAVIOR

Observation Type:
Traveling   Stationary   Historical   Incidental   Other

☐   ☐   ☐   ☐   ☐

Birding Observations/Extra Notes
Describe any important information about the bird or species

SKETCH OR ATTACH A PHOTO OF ANY SPECIES SPECIFIC DETAILS (Image of the bird, anatomy, size, feathers etc.)

Scientific Name of Bird/Species _____

Family Name: _____

Observation Date: _____

Time/Duration: _____

Location: _____

Distance: _____

Weather: _____

Number Seen: _____ Male(s) _____ Female(s)

Sounds: _____

Party Size: _____

Other species also spotted in the area:

- _____

- _____

- _____

- _____

- _____

Observation Type:

Traveling ☐   Stationary ☐   Historical ☐   Incidental ☐   Other ☐

HABITAT

BEHAVIOR

Birding Observations/Extra Notes

Describe any important information about the bird or species

_____

_____

_____

_____

_____

_____

_____

_____

_____

_____

_____

_____

_____

_____

_____

_____

_____

_____

_____

_____

_____

_____

_____

_____

_____

_____

_____

_____

_____

SKETCH OR ATTACH A PHOTO OF ANY SPECIES SPECIFIC DETAILS (Image of the bird, anatomy, size, feathers etc.)

Scientific Name of Bird/Species _____

Family Name: _____

Observation Date: _____

Time/Duration: _____

Location: _____

Distance: _____

Weather: _____

Number Seen: _____ Male(s) _____ Female(s)

Sounds: _____

Party Size: _____

Other species also spotted in the area:

- _____
- _____
- _____
- _____
- _____

Observation Type:

Traveling Stationary Historical Incidental Other
☐ ☐ ☐ ☐ ☐

HABITAT

BEHAVIOR

Birding Observations/Extra Notes
Describe any important information about the bird or species

SKETCH OR ATTACH A PHOTO OF ANY SPECIES SPECIFIC DETAILS (Image of the bird, anatomy, size, feathers etc.)

Scientific Name of Bird/Species _____

Family Name: _____

Observation Date: _____

Time/Duration: _____

Location: _____

Distance: _____

Weather: _____

Number Seen: _____ Male(s) _____ Female(s)

Sounds: _____

Party Size: _____

Other species also spotted in the area:

- _____

- _____

- _____

- _____

- _____

Observation Type:

Traveling ☐   Stationary ☐   Historical ☐   Incidental ☐   Other ☐

HABITAT

BEHAVIOR

Birding Observations/Extra Notes

Describe any important information about the bird or species

SKETCH OR ATTACH A PHOTO OF ANY SPECIES SPECIFIC DETAILS (Image of the bird, anatomy, size, feathers etc.)

Scientific Name of Bird/Species _____

Family Name: _____

Observation Date: _____

Time/Duration: _____

Location: _____

Distance: _____

Weather: _____

Number Seen: _____ Male(s) _____ Female(s)

Sounds: _____

Party Size: _____

Other species also spotted in the area:

- _____
- _____
- _____
- _____
- _____

Observation Type:

Traveling Stationary Historical Incidental Other
☐   ☐   ☐   ☐   ☐

HABITAT

BEHAVIOR

Birding Observations/Extra Notes
Describe any important information about the bird or species

SKETCH OR ATTACH A PHOTO OF ANY SPECIES SPECIFIC DETAILS (Image of the bird, anatomy, size, feathers etc.)

Scientific Name of Bird/Species _____

Family Name: _____

Observation Date: _____

Time/Duration: _____

Location: _____

Distance: _____

Weather: _____

Number Seen: _____ Male(s) _____ Female(s)

Sounds: _____

Party Size: _____

Other species also spotted in the area:

- _____
- _____
- _____
- _____
- _____

Observation Type:

Traveling   Stationary   Historical   Incidental   Other
☐   ☐   ☐   ☐   ☐

HABITAT

BEHAVIOR

Birding Observations/Extra Notes

Describe any important information about the bird or species

_____

_____

_____

_____

_____

_____

_____

_____

_____

_____

_____

_____

_____

_____

_____

_____

_____

_____

_____

_____

_____

_____

_____

_____

_____

_____

_____

_____

_____

_____

_____

SKETCH OR ATTACH A PHOTO OF ANY SPECIES SPECIFIC DETAILS (Image of the bird, anatomy, size, feathers etc.)

Scientific Name of Bird/Species _____

Family Name: _____

Observation Date: _____

Time/Duration: _____

Location: _____

Distance: _____

Weather: _____

Number Seen: _____ Male(s) _____ Female(s)

Sounds: _____

Party Size: _____

Other species also spotted in the area:

- _____
- _____
- _____
- _____
- _____

Observation Type:

Traveling ☐   Stationary ☐   Historical ☐   Incidental ☐   Other ☐

HABITAT

BEHAVIOR

Birding Observations/Extra Notes
Describe any important information about the bird or species

_____

_____

_____

_____

_____

_____

_____

_____

_____

_____

_____

_____

_____

_____

_____

_____

_____

_____

_____

_____

_____

_____

_____

_____

_____

_____

_____

_____

SKETCH OR ATTACH A PHOTO OF ANY SPECIES SPECIFIC DETAILS (Image of the bird, anatomy, size, feathers etc.)

Scientific Name of Bird/Species _____

Family Name: _____

Observation Date: _____

Time/Duration: _____

Location: _____

Distance: _____

Weather: _____

Number Seen: _____ Male(s) _____ Female(s)

Sounds: _____

Party Size: _____

Other species also spotted in the area:

- _____
- _____
- _____
- _____
- _____

Observation Type:

Traveling ☐   Stationary ☐   Historical ☐   Incidental ☐   Other ☐

HABITAT

BEHAVIOR

Birding Observations/Extra Notes

Describe any important information about the bird or species

SKETCH OR ATTACH A PHOTO OF ANY SPECIES SPECIFIC DETAILS (Image of the bird, anatomy, size, feathers etc.)

Scientific Name of Bird/Species _____

Family Name: _____   HABITAT

Observation Date: _____

Time/Duration: _____

Location: _____

Distance: _____

Weather: _____

Number Seen: _____ Male(s) _____ Female(s)

Sounds: _____

Party Size: _____

Other species also spotted in the area: BEHAVIOR

- _____

- _____

- _____

- _____

- _____

Observation Type:

Traveling   Stationary   Historical   Incidental   Other
☐   ☐   ☐   ☐   ☐

Birding Observations/Extra Notes

Describe any important information about the bird or species

COMMON NAME OF BIRD / SPECIES

SKETCH OR ATTACH A PHOTO OF ANY SPECIES SPECIFIC DETAILS (Image of the bird, anatomy, size, feathers etc.)

Scientific Name of Bird/Species _____

Family Name: _____

Observation Date: _____

Time/Duration: _____

Location: _____

Distance: _____

Weather: _____

Number Seen: _____ Male(s) _____ Female(s)

Sounds: _____

Party Size: _____

Other species also spotted in the area:

- _____
- _____
- _____
- _____
- _____

Observation Type:

Traveling ☐   Stationary ☐   Historical ☐   Incidental ☐   Other ☐

HABITAT

BEHAVIOR

Birding Observations/Extra Notes
Describe any important information about the bird or species

SKETCH OR ATTACH A PHOTO OF ANY SPECIES SPECIFIC DETAILS (Image of the bird, anatomy, size, feathers etc.)

Scientific Name of Bird/Species _____

Family Name: _____

Observation Date: _____

Time/Duration: _____

Location: _____

Distance: _____

Weather: _____

Number Seen: _____ Male(s) _____ Female(s)

Sounds: _____

Party Size: _____

Other species also spotted in the area:

- _____
- _____
- _____
- _____
- _____

Observation Type:

Traveling   Stationary   Historical   Incidental   Other
☐   ☐   ☐   ☐   ☐

HABITAT

BEHAVIOR

Birding Observations/Extra Notes
Describe any important information about the bird or species

SKETCH OR ATTACH A PHOTO OF ANY SPECIES SPECIFIC DETAILS (Image of the bird, anatomy, size, feathers etc.)

Scientific Name of Bird/Species _____

Family Name: _____

Observation Date: _____

Time/Duration: _____

Location: _____

Distance: _____

Weather: _____

Number Seen: _____ Male(s) _____ Female(s)

Sounds: _____

Party Size: _____

Other species also spotted in the area:

- _____
- _____
- _____
- _____
- _____

Observation Type:

Traveling ☐   Stationary ☐   Historical ☐   Incidental ☐   Other ☐

HABITAT

BEHAVIOR

Birding Observations/Extra Notes

Describe any important information about the bird or species

SKETCH OR ATTACH A PHOTO OF ANY SPECIES SPECIFIC DETAILS (Image of the bird, anatomy, size, feathers etc.)

Scientific Name of Bird/Species _____

Family Name: _____

Observation Date: _____

Time/Duration: _____

Location: _____

Distance: _____

Weather: _____

Number Seen: _____ Male(s) _____ Female(s)

Sounds: _____

Party Size: _____

Other species also spotted in the area:

- _____
- _____
- _____
- _____
- _____

Observation Type:

Traveling Stationary Historical Incidental Other
☐　　　☐　　　☐　　　☐　　　☐

HABITAT

BEHAVIOR

Birding Observations/Extra Notes

Describe any important information about the bird or species

SKETCH OR ATTACH A PHOTO OF ANY SPECIES SPECIFIC DETAILS (Image of the bird, anatomy, size, feathers etc.)

Scientific Name of Bird/Species _____

Family Name: _____

Observation Date: _____

Time/Duration: _____

Location: _____

Distance: _____

Weather: _____

Number Seen: _____ Male(s) _____ Female(s)

Sounds: _____

Party Size: _____

Other species also spotted in the area:

- _____
- _____
- _____
- _____
- _____

Observation Type:

Traveling ☐ Stationary ☐ Historical ☐ Incidental ☐ Other ☐

HABITAT

BEHAVIOR

Birding Observations/Extra Notes
Describe any important information about the bird or species

SKETCH OR ATTACH A PHOTO OF ANY SPECIES SPECIFIC DETAILS (Image of the bird, anatomy, size, feathers etc.)

Scientific Name of Bird/Species _____

Family Name: _____

Observation Date: _____

Time/Duration: _____

Location: _____

Distance: _____

Weather: _____

Number Seen: ___ Male(s) ___ Female(s)

Sounds: _____

Party Size: _____

Other species also spotted in the area:

- _____
- _____
- _____
- _____
- _____

Observation Type:

Traveling ☐ Stationary ☐ Historical ☐ Incidental ☐ Other ☐

HABITAT

BEHAVIOR

Birding Observations/Extra Notes

Describe any important information about the bird or species

SKETCH OR ATTACH A PHOTO OF ANY SPECIES SPECIFIC DETAILS (Image of the bird, anatomy, size, feathers etc.)

Scientific Name of Bird/Species _____

Family Name: _____

Observation Date: _____

Time/Duration: _____

Location: _____

Distance: _____

Weather: _____

Number Seen: _____ Male(s) _____ Female(s)

Sounds: _____

Party Size: _____

Other species also spotted in the area:

- _____
- _____
- _____
- _____
- _____

Observation Type:

Traveling ☐   Stationary ☐   Historical ☐   Incidental ☐   Other ☐

HABITAT

BEHAVIOR

Birding Observations/Extra Notes
Describe any important information about the bird or species

SKETCH OR ATTACH A PHOTO OF ANY SPECIES SPECIFIC DETAILS (Image of the bird, anatomy, size, feathers etc.)

Scientific Name of Bird/Species _____

Family Name: _____

Observation Date: _____

Time/Duration: _____

Location: _____

Distance: _____

Weather: _____

Number Seen: _____ Male(s) _____ Female(s)

Sounds: _____

Party Size: _____

Other species also spotted in the area:

- _____

- _____

- _____

- _____

- _____

Observation Type:

Traveling   Stationary   Historical   Incidental   Other

☐   ☐   ☐   ☐   ☐

HABITAT

BEHAVIOR

Birding Observations/Extra Notes

Describe any important information about the bird or species

SKETCH OR ATTACH A PHOTO OF ANY SPECIES SPECIFIC DETAILS (Image of the bird, anatomy, size, feathers etc.)

Scientific Name of Bird/Species _____

Family Name: _____

Observation Date: _____

Time/Duration: _____

Location: _____

Distance: _____

Weather: _____

Number Seen: _____ Male(s) _____ Female(s)

Sounds: _____

Party Size: _____

Other species also spotted in the area:

- _____

- _____

- _____

- _____

- _____

HABITAT

BEHAVIOR

Observation Type:

Traveling Stationary Historical Incidental Other
☐   ☐   ☐   ☐   ☐

Birding Observations/Extra Notes

Describe any important information about the bird or species

SKETCH OR ATTACH A PHOTO OF ANY SPECIES SPECIFIC DETAILS (Image of the bird, anatomy, size, feathers etc.)

Scientific Name of Bird/Species _____

Family Name: _____

Observation Date: _____

Time/Duration: _____

Location: _____

Distance: _____

Weather: _____

Number Seen: _____ Male(s) _____ Female(s)

Sounds: _____

Party Size: _____

Other species also spotted in the area:

- _____

- _____

- _____

- _____

- _____

Observation Type:

Traveling ☐   Stationary ☐   Historical ☐   Incidental ☐   Other ☐

HABITAT

BEHAVIOR

Birding Observations/Extra Notes

Describe any important information about the bird or species

_____

_____

_____

_____

_____

_____

_____

_____

_____

_____

_____

_____

_____

_____

_____

_____

_____

_____

_____

_____

_____

_____

_____

_____

_____

_____

_____

_____

_____

SKETCH OR ATTACH A PHOTO OF ANY SPECIES SPECIFIC DETAILS (Image of the bird, anatomy, size, feathers etc.)

Scientific Name of Bird/Species _____

Family Name: _____

Observation Date: _____

Time/Duration: _____

Location: _____

Distance: _____

Weather: _____

Number Seen: _____ Male(s) _____ Female(s)

Sounds: _____

Party Size: _____

Other species also spotted in the area:

- _____
- _____
- _____
- _____
- _____

Observation Type:

Traveling ☐ Stationary ☐ Historical ☐ Incidental ☐ Other ☐

HABITAT

BEHAVIOR

Birding Observations/Extra Notes

Describe any important information about the bird or species

SKETCH OR ATTACH A PHOTO OF ANY SPECIES SPECIFIC DETAILS (Image of the bird, anatomy, size, feathers etc.)

Scientific Name of Bird/Species _____

Family Name: _____

Observation Date: _____

Time/Duration: _____

Location: _____

Distance: _____

Weather: _____

Number Seen: _____ Male(s) _____ Female(s)

Sounds: _____

Party Size: _____

Other species also spotted in the area:

- _____
- _____
- _____
- _____
- _____

Observation Type:

Traveling ☐   Stationary ☐   Historical ☐   Incidental ☐   Other ☐

HABITAT

BEHAVIOR

Birding Observations/Extra Notes
Describe any important information about the bird or species

SKETCH OR ATTACH A PHOTO OF ANY SPECIES SPECIFIC DETAILS (Image of the bird, anatomy, size, feathers etc.)

Scientific Name of Bird/Species _____

Family Name: _____

Observation Date: _____

Time/Duration: _____

Location: _____

Distance: _____

Weather: _____

Number Seen: _____ Male(s) _____ Female(s)

Sounds: _____

Party Size: _____

Other species also spotted in the area:

- _____
- _____
- _____
- _____
- _____

Observation Type:

Traveling ☐   Stationary ☐   Historical ☐   Incidental ☐   Other ☐

HABITAT

BEHAVIOR

Birding Observations/Extra Notes

Describe any important information about the bird or species

_____

_____

_____

_____

_____

_____

_____

_____

_____

_____

_____

_____

_____

_____

_____

_____

_____

_____

_____

_____

_____

_____

_____

_____

_____

_____

_____

_____

_____

SKETCH OR ATTACH A PHOTO OF ANY SPECIES SPECIFIC DETAILS (Image of the bird, anatomy, size, feathers etc.)

Scientific Name of Bird/Species _____

Family Name: _____

Observation Date: _____

Time/Duration: _____

Location: _____

Distance: _____

Weather: _____

Number Seen: _____ Male(s) _____ Female(s)

Sounds: _____

Party Size: _____

Other species also spotted in the area:

- _____
- _____
- _____
- _____
- _____

Observation Type:

Traveling Stationary Historical Incidental Other
☐ ☐ ☐ ☐ ☐

HABITAT

BEHAVIOR

Birding Observations/Extra Notes

Describe any important information about the bird or species

COMMON NAME OF BIRD / SPECIES

SKETCH OR ATTACH A PHOTO OF ANY SPECIES SPECIFIC DETAILS (Image of the bird, anatomy, size, feathers etc.)

Scientific Name of Bird/Species _____

Family Name: _____

Observation Date: _____

Time/Duration: _____

Location: _____

Distance: _____

Weather: _____

Number Seen: _____ Male(s) _____ Female(s)

Sounds: _____

Party Size: _____

Other species also spotted in the area:

- _____
- _____
- _____
- _____
- _____

HABITAT

BEHAVIOR

Observation Type:

Traveling ☐　Stationary ☐　Historical ☐　Incidental ☐　Other ☐

Birding Observations/Extra Notes
Describe any important information about the bird or species

SKETCH OR ATTACH A PHOTO OF ANY SPECIES SPECIFIC DETAILS (Image of the bird, anatomy, size, feathers etc.)

Scientific Name of Bird/Species _____

Family Name: _____

Observation Date: _____

Time/Duration: _____

Location: _____

Distance: _____

Weather: _____

Number Seen: _____ Male(s) _____ Female(s)

Sounds: _____

Party Size: _____

Other species also spotted in the area:

- _____
- _____
- _____
- _____
- _____

Observation Type:

Traveling ☐ Stationary ☐ Historical ☐ Incidental ☐ Other ☐

HABITAT

BEHAVIOR

Birding Observations/Extra Notes

Describe any important information about the bird or species

SKETCH OR ATTACH A PHOTO OF ANY SPECIES SPECIFIC DETAILS (Image of the bird, anatomy, size, feathers etc.)

Scientific Name of Bird/Species _____

Family Name: _____

Observation Date: _____

Time/Duration: _____

Location: _____

Distance: _____

Weather: _____

Number Seen: _____ Male(s) _____ Female(s)

Sounds: _____

Party Size: _____

Other species also spotted in the area:

- _____
- _____
- _____
- _____
- _____

Observation Type:

Traveling ☐ Stationary ☐ Historical ☐ Incidental ☐ Other ☐

HABITAT

BEHAVIOR

Birding Observations/Extra Notes

Describe any important information about the bird or species

SKETCH OR ATTACH A PHOTO OF ANY SPECIES SPECIFIC DETAILS (Image of the bird, anatomy, size, feathers etc.)

Scientific Name of Bird/Species _____

Family Name: _____

Observation Date: _____

Time/Duration: _____

Location: _____

Distance: _____

Weather: _____

Number Seen: _____ Male(s) _____ Female(s)

Sounds: _____

Party Size: _____

Other species also spotted in the area:

- _____
- _____
- _____
- _____
- _____

Observation Type:

Traveling Stationary Historical Incidental Other
   ☐   ☐   ☐   ☐   ☐

HABITAT

BEHAVIOR

Birding Observations/Extra Notes
Describe any important information about the bird or species

SKETCH OR ATTACH A PHOTO OF ANY SPECIES SPECIFIC DETAILS (Image of the bird, anatomy, size, feathers etc.)

Scientific Name of Bird/Species _____

Family Name: _____

Observation Date: _____

Time/Duration: _____

Location: _____

Distance: _____

Weather: _____

Number Seen: _____ Male(s) _____ Female(s)

Sounds: _____

Party Size: _____

Other species also spotted in the area:

- _____
- _____
- _____
- _____
- _____

Observation Type:

Traveling ☐ Stationary ☐ Historical ☐ Incidental ☐ Other ☐

HABITAT

BEHAVIOR

Birding Observations/Extra Notes

Describe any important information about the bird or species

_____
_____
_____
_____
_____
_____
_____
_____
_____
_____
_____
_____
_____
_____
_____
_____
_____
_____
_____
_____
_____
_____
_____
_____
_____
_____
_____
_____

SKETCH OR ATTACH A PHOTO OF ANY SPECIES SPECIFIC DETAILS (Image of the bird, anatomy, size, feathers etc.)

Scientific Name of Bird/Species _____

Family Name: _____

Observation Date: _____

Time/Duration: _____

Location: _____

Distance: _____

Weather: _____

Number Seen: _____ Male(s) _____ Female(s)

Sounds: _____

Party Size: _____

Other species also spotted in the area:

- _____
- _____
- _____
- _____
- _____

Observation Type:

Traveling ☐ Stationary ☐ Historical ☐ Incidental ☐ Other ☐

HABITAT

BEHAVIOR

Birding Observations/Extra Notes

Describe any important information about the bird or species

SKETCH OR ATTACH A PHOTO OF ANY SPECIES SPECIFIC DETAILS (Image of the bird, anatomy, size, feathers etc.)

Scientific Name of Bird/Species _____

Family Name: _____

Observation Date: _____

Time/Duration: _____

Location: _____

Distance: _____

Weather: _____

Number Seen: _____ Male(s) _____ Female(s)

Sounds: _____

Party Size: _____

Other species also spotted in the area:

- _____

- _____

- _____

- _____

- _____

Observation Type:

Traveling Stationary Historical Incidental Other
☐   ☐   ☐   ☐   ☐

HABITAT

BEHAVIOR

Birding Observations/Extra Notes

Describe any important information about the bird or species

SKETCH OR ATTACH A PHOTO OF ANY SPECIES SPECIFIC DETAILS (Image of the bird, anatomy, size, feathers etc.)

Scientific Name of Bird/Species _____

Family Name: _____

Observation Date: _____

Time/Duration: _____

Location: _____

Distance: _____

Weather: _____

Number Seen: _____ Male(s) _____ Female(s)

Sounds: _____

Party Size: _____

Other species also spotted in the area:

- _____
- _____
- _____
- _____
- _____

Observation Type:

Traveling Stationary Historical Incidental Other
☐   ☐   ☐   ☐   ☐

HABITAT

BEHAVIOR

Birding Observations/Extra Notes

Describe any important information about the bird or species

87 | Field Guide Notes for the _____

COMMON NAME OF BIRD / SPECIES

SKETCH OR ATTACH A PHOTO OF ANY SPECIES SPECIFIC DETAILS (Image of the bird, anatomy, size, feathers etc.)

Scientific Name of Bird/Species _____

Family Name: _____

Observation Date: _____

Time/Duration: _____

Location: _____

Distance: _____

Weather: _____

Number Seen: _____ Male(s) _____ Female(s)

Sounds: _____

Party Size: _____

Other species also spotted in the area:

- _____
- _____
- _____
- _____
- _____

Observation Type:

Traveling ☐ Stationary ☐ Historical ☐ Incidental ☐ Other ☐

HABITAT

BEHAVIOR

Birding Observations/Extra Notes

Describe any important information about the bird or species

SKETCH OR ATTACH A PHOTO OF ANY SPECIES SPECIFIC DETAILS (Image of the bird, anatomy, size, feathers etc.)

Scientific Name of Bird/Species _____

Family Name: _____

Observation Date: _____

Time/Duration: _____

Location: _____

Distance: _____

Weather: _____

Number Seen: _____ Male(s) _____ Female(s)

Sounds: _____

Party Size: _____

Other species also spotted in the area:

- _____
- _____
- _____
- _____
- _____

Observation Type:

Traveling ☐   Stationary ☐   Historical ☐   Incidental ☐   Other ☐

HABITAT

BEHAVIOR

Birding Observations/Extra Notes
Describe any important information about the bird or species

SKETCH OR ATTACH A PHOTO OF ANY SPECIES SPECIFIC DETAILS (Image of the bird, anatomy, size, feathers etc.)

Scientific Name of Bird/Species _____

Family Name: _____

Observation Date: _____

Time/Duration: _____

Location: _____

Distance: _____

Weather: _____

Number Seen: _____ Male(s) _____ Female(s)

Sounds: _____

Party Size: _____

Other species also spotted in the area:

- _____
- _____
- _____
- _____
- _____

Observation Type:

Traveling   Stationary   Historical   Incidental   Other
☐   ☐   ☐   ☐   ☐

HABITAT

BEHAVIOR

Birding Observations/Extra Notes

Describe any important information about the bird or species

SKETCH OR ATTACH A PHOTO OF ANY SPECIES SPECIFIC DETAILS (Image of the bird, anatomy, size, feathers etc.)

Scientific Name of Bird/Species _____

Family Name: _____

Observation Date: _____

Time/Duration: _____

Location: _____

Distance: _____

Weather: _____

Number Seen: _____ Male(s) _____ Female(s)

Sounds: _____

Party Size: _____

Other species also spotted in the area:

- _____
- _____
- _____
- _____
- _____

HABITAT

BEHAVIOR

Observation Type:

Traveling ☐ Stationary ☐ Historical ☐ Incidental ☐ Other ☐

Birding Observations/Extra Notes

Describe any important information about the bird or species

_____

_____

_____

_____

_____

_____

_____

_____

_____

_____

_____

_____

_____

_____

_____

_____

_____

_____

_____

_____

_____

_____

_____

_____

_____

_____

_____

SKETCH OR ATTACH A PHOTO OF ANY SPECIES SPECIFIC DETAILS (Image of the bird, anatomy, size, feathers etc.)

Scientific Name of Bird/Species _____

Family Name: _____

Observation Date: _____

Time/Duration: _____

Location: _____

Distance: _____

Weather: _____

Number Seen: _____ Male(s) _____ Female(s)

Sounds: _____

Party Size: _____

Other species also spotted in the area:

- _____
- _____
- _____
- _____
- _____

HABITAT

BEHAVIOR

Observation Type:

Traveling ☐ Stationary ☐ Historical ☐ Incidental ☐ Other ☐

Birding Observations/Extra Notes

Describe any important information about the bird or species

SKETCH OR ATTACH A PHOTO OF ANY SPECIES SPECIFIC DETAILS (Image of the bird, anatomy, size, feathers etc.)

Scientific Name of Bird/Species _____

Family Name: _____

Observation Date: _____

Time/Duration: _____

Location: _____

Distance: _____

Weather: _____

Number Seen: _____ Male(s) _____ Female(s)

Sounds: _____

Party Size: _____

Other species also spotted in the area:

- _____
- _____
- _____
- _____
- _____

Observation Type:

Traveling ☐ Stationary ☐ Historical ☐ Incidental ☐ Other ☐

HABITAT

BEHAVIOR

Birding Observations/Extra Notes

Describe any important information about the bird or species

_____
_____
_____
_____
_____
_____
_____
_____
_____
_____
_____
_____
_____
_____
_____
_____
_____
_____
_____
_____
_____
_____
_____
_____
_____
_____
_____
_____
_____

SKETCH OR ATTACH A PHOTO OF ANY SPECIES SPECIFIC DETAILS (Image of the bird, anatomy, size, feathers etc.)

Scientific Name of Bird/Species _____

Family Name: _____

Observation Date: _____

Time/Duration: _____

Location: _____

Distance: _____

Weather: _____

Number Seen: _____ Male(s) _____ Female(s)

Sounds: _____

Party Size: _____

Other species also spotted in the area:

- _____
- _____
- _____
- _____
- _____

Observation Type:

Traveling ☐   Stationary ☐   Historical ☐   Incidental ☐   Other ☐

HABITAT

BEHAVIOR

Birding Observations/Extra Notes

Describe any important information about the bird or species

SKETCH OR ATTACH A PHOTO OF ANY SPECIES SPECIFIC DETAILS (Image of the bird, anatomy, size, feathers etc.)

Scientific Name of Bird/Species _____

Family Name: _____

Observation Date: _____

Time/Duration: _____

Location: _____

Distance: _____

Weather: _____

Number Seen: _____ Male(s) _____ Female(s)

Sounds: _____

Party Size: _____

Other species also spotted in the area:

- _____
- _____
- _____
- _____
- _____

Observation Type:

Traveling   Stationary   Historical   Incidental   Other

☐   ☐   ☐   ☐   ☐

HABITAT

BEHAVIOR

Birding Observations/Extra Notes

Describe any important information about the bird or species

_____

_____

_____

_____

_____

_____

_____

_____

_____

_____

_____

_____

_____

_____

_____

_____

_____

_____

_____

_____

_____

_____

_____

_____

_____

_____

_____

_____

_____

COMMON NAME OF BIRD / SPECIES

SKETCH OR ATTACH A PHOTO OF ANY SPECIES SPECIFIC DETAILS (Image of the bird, anatomy, size, feathers etc.)

Scientific Name of Bird/Species _____

Family Name: _____

Observation Date: _____

Time/Duration: _____

Location: _____

Distance: _____

Weather: _____

Number Seen: _____ Male(s) _____ Female(s)

Sounds: _____

Party Size: _____

Other species also spotted in the area:

- _____
- _____
- _____
- _____
- _____

Observation Type:

Traveling ☐　Stationary ☐　Historical ☐　Incidental ☐　Other ☐

HABITAT

BEHAVIOR

Birding Observations/Extra Notes
Describe any important information about the bird or species

COMMON NAME OF BIRD / SPECIES

SKETCH OR ATTACH A PHOTO OF ANY SPECIES SPECIFIC DETAILS (Image of the bird, anatomy, size, feathers etc.)

Scientific Name of Bird/Species _____

Family Name: _____

Observation Date: _____

Time/Duration: _____

Location: _____

Distance: _____

Weather: _____

Number Seen: _____ Male(s) _____ Female(s)

Sounds: _____

Party Size: _____

Other species also spotted in the area:

- _____
- _____
- _____
- _____
- _____

Observation Type:

Traveling ☐ Stationary ☐ Historical ☐ Incidental ☐ Other ☐

HABITAT

BEHAVIOR

Birding Observations/Extra Notes
Describe any important information about the bird or species

SKETCH OR ATTACH A PHOTO OF ANY SPECIES SPECIFIC DETAILS (Image of the bird, anatomy, size, feathers etc.)

Scientific Name of Bird/Species _____
Family Name: _____
Observation Date: _____
Time/Duration: _____
Location: _____
Distance: _____
Weather: _____
Number Seen: _____ Male(s) _____ Female(s)
Sounds: _____
Party Size: _____
Other species also spotted in the area:
- _____
- _____
- _____
- _____
- _____

Observation Type:
Traveling Stationary Historical Incidental Other
☐   ☐   ☐   ☐   ☐

HABITAT

BEHAVIOR

Birding Observations/Extra Notes

Describe any important information about the bird or species

SKETCH OR ATTACH A PHOTO OF ANY SPECIES SPECIFIC DETAILS (Image of the bird, anatomy, size, feathers etc.)

Scientific Name of Bird/Species _____

Family Name: _____

Observation Date: _____

Time/Duration: _____

Location: _____

Distance: _____

Weather: _____

Number Seen: _____ Male(s) _____ Female(s)

Sounds: _____

Party Size: _____

Other species also spotted in the area:

- _____
- _____
- _____
- _____
- _____

Observation Type:
Traveling   Stationary   Historical   Incidental   Other
☐   ☐   ☐   ☐   ☐

HABITAT

BEHAVIOR

Birding Observations/Extra Notes

Describe any important information about the bird or species

99 | Field Guide Notes for the _____
COMMON NAME OF BIRD / SPECIES

SKETCH OR ATTACH A PHOTO OF ANY SPECIES SPECIFIC DETAILS (Image of the bird, anatomy, size, feathers etc.)

Scientific Name of Bird/Species _____
Family Name: _____
Observation Date: _____
Time/Duration: _____
Location: _____
Distance: _____
Weather: _____
Number Seen: ____ Male(s) ____ Female(s)
Sounds: _____
Party Size: _____
Other species also spotted in the area:
- _____
- _____
- _____
- _____
- _____

Observation Type:
Traveling ☐ Stationary ☐ Historical ☐ Incidental ☐ Other ☐

HABITAT

BEHAVIOR

Birding Observations/Extra Notes

Describe any important information about the bird or species

COMMON NAME OF BIRD / SPECIES

SKETCH OR ATTACH A PHOTO OF ANY SPECIES SPECIFIC DETAILS (Image of the bird, anatomy, size, feathers etc.)

Scientific Name of Bird/Species _____

Family Name: _____

Observation Date: _____

Time/Duration: _____

Location: _____

Distance: _____

Weather: _____

Number Seen: _____ Male(s) _____ Female(s)

Sounds: _____

Party Size: _____

Other species also spotted in the area:

- _____
- _____
- _____
- _____
- _____

HABITAT

BEHAVIOR

Observation Type:

Traveling □   Stationary □   Historical □   Incidental □   Other □

Birding Observations/Extra Notes
Describe any important information about the bird or species

PAGE ALBATROSSES
Order: Procellariiformes, Family: Diomedeidae

Black-footed Albatross
Phoebastria nigripes

Laysan Albatross
Phoebastria immutabilis

PAGE ANHINGAS
Order: Suliformes, Family: Anhingidae

Anhinga
Anhinga anhinga

PAGE AUKS, MURRES, AND PUFFINS
Order: Charadriiformes, Family: Alcidae

Ancient Murrelet
Synthliboramphus antiquus

Atlantic Puffin
Fratercula arctica

Black Guillemot
Cepphus grylle

Cassin's Auklet
Ptychoramphus aleuticus

Common Murre
Uria aalge

Crested Auklet
Aethia cristatella

Common Murre
Uria aalge

Dovekie
Alle alle

Great Auk
Pinguinus impennis

Horned Puffin
Fratercula corniculata

Kittlitz's Murrelet
Brachyramphus brevirostris

Least Auklet
Aethia pusilla

Marbled Murrelet
Brachyramphus marmoratus

Parakeet Auklet
Aethia psittacula

Pigeon Guillemot
Cepphus columba

Razorbill
Alca torda

Rhinoceros Auklet
Cerorhinca monocerata

Scripps's Murrelet
Synthliboramphus scrippsi

Thick-billed Murre
Uria lomvia

Tufted Puffin
Fratercula cirrhata

Whiskered Auklet
Aethia pygmaea

PAGE BARN-OWLS
Order: Strigiformes, Family: Tytonidae

Barn Owl
Tyto alba

PAGE BOOBIES AND GANNETS
Order: Suliformes, Family: Tytonidae

Brown Booby
Sula leucogaster

Masked Booby
Sula dactylatra

Northern Gannet
Morus bassanus

Red-footed Booby
Sula sula

PAGE BULBULS
Order: Passeriformes, Family: Pycnonotidae

Red-vented Bulbul
Pycnonotus cafer

Red-whiskered Bulbul
Pycnonotus jocosus

PAGE CARDINALS AND ALLIES
Order: Passeriformes, Family: Cardinalidae

Black-headed Grosbeak
Pheucticus melanocephalus

Blue Grosbeak
Passerina caerulea

Dickcissel
Spiza americana

Hepatic Tanager
Piranga flava

Indigo Bunting
Passerina cyanea

Lazuli Bunting
Passerina amoena

Northern Cardinal
Cardinalis cardinalis

Painted Bunting
Passerina ciris

Pyrrhuloxia
Cardinalis sinuatus

Rose-breasted Grosbeak
Pheucticus ludovicianus

Scarlet Tanager
Piranga olivacea

Summer Tanager
Piranga rubra

Varied Bunting
Passerina versicolor

Western Tanager
Piranga ludoviciana

PAGE CORMORANTS AND SHAGS
Order: Suliformes, Family: Phalacrocoracidae

Brandt's Cormorant
Phalacrocorax penicillatus

Double-crested Cormorant
Phalacrocorax auritus

Great Cormorant
Phalacrocorax carbo

Neotropic Cormorant
Phalacrocorax brasilianus

Pelagic Cormorant
Phalacrocorax pelagicus

Red-faced Cormorant
Phalacrocorax urile

PAGE CRANES
Order: Gruiformes, Family: Gruidae

Sandhill Crane
Antigone canadensis

Whooping Crane
Grus americana

PAGE CROWS, JAYS AND MAGPIES
Order: Passeriformes, Family: Corvidae

American Crow
Corvus brachyrhynchos

Black-billed Magpie
Pica hudsonia

Blue Jay
Cyanocitta cristata

California Scrub-Jay
Aphelocoma californica

Canada Jay
Perisoreus canadensis

Chihuahuan Raven
Corvus cryptoleucus

Clark's Nutcracker
Nucifraga columbiana

Common Raven
Corvus corax

Fish Crow
Corvus ossifragus

Florida Scrub-Jay
Aphelocoma coerulescens

Green Jay
Cyanocorax yncas

Hawaiian Crow
Corvus hawaiiensis

Island Scrub-Jay
Aphelocoma insularis

Mexican Jay
Aphelocoma wollweberi

Northwestern Crow
Corvus caurinus

Pinyon Jay
Gymnorhinus cyanocephalus

Steller's Jay
Cyanocitta stelleri

Woodhouse's Scrub-Jay
Aphelocoma woodhouseii

Yellow-billed Magpie
Pica nuttalli

CUCKOOS
PAGE | Order: Cuculiformes, Family: Cuculidae

Black-billed Cuckoo
Coccyzus erythropthalmus

Greater Roadrunner
Geococcyx californianus

Groove-billed Ani
Crotophaga sulcirostris

Mangrove Cuckoo
Coccyzus minor

Smooth-billed Ani
Crotophaga ani

Yellow-billed Cuckoo
Coccyzus americanus

DIPPERS
PAGE | Order: Passeriformes, Family: Cinclidae

American Dipper
Cinclus mexicanus

DUCKS, GEESE, AND WATERFOWL (1)
PAGE | Order: Anseriformes, Family: Anatidae

American Black Duck
Anas rubripes

American Wigeon
Mareca americana

Barrow's Goldeneye
Bucephala islandica

Black Scoter
Melanitta americana

Black-bellied Whistling-Duck
Dendrocygna autumnalis

Blue-winged Teal
Spatula discors

Brant
Branta bernicla

Bufflehead
Bucephala albeola

Cackling Goose
Branta hutchinsii

Canada Goose
Branta canadensis

Canvasback
Aythya valisineria

Cinnamon Teal
Spatula cyanoptera

Common Eider
Somateria mollissima

Common Goldeneye
Bucephala clangula

Common Merganser
Mergus merganser

Egyptian Goose
Alopochen aegyptiaca

Emperor Goose
Anser canagicus

Fulvous Whistling-Duck
Dendrocygna bicolor

Gadwall
Mareca strepera

Greater Scaup
Aythya marila

Greater White-fronted Goose
Anser albifrons

Green-winged Teal
Anas crecca

DUCKS, GEESE, AND WATERFOWL (2)
PAGE | Order: Anseriformes, Family: Anatidae

Harlequin Duck
Histrionicus histrionicus

Hawaiian Duck
Anas wyvilliana

Hawaiian Goose
Branta sandvicensis

Hooded Merganser
Lophodytes cucullatus

King Eider
Somateria spectabilis

Labrador Duck
Camptorhynchus labradorius

Laysan Duck
Anas laysanensis

Lesser Scaup
Aythya affinis

Long-tailed Duck
Clangula hyemalis

Mallard Anas
platyrhynchos

Masked Duck
Nomonyx dominicus

Mottled Duck
Anas fulvigula

Mute Swan
Cygnus olor

Northern Pintail
Anas acuta

Northern Shoveler
Spatula clypeata

Red-breasted Merganser
Mergus serrator

Redhead
Aythya americana

Ring-necked Duck
Aythya collaris

Ross's Goose
Anser rossii

Ruddy Duck
Oxyura jamaicensis

Snow Goose
Anser caerulescens

Spectacled Eider
Somateria fischeri

Steller's Eider
Polysticta stelleri

Surf Scoter
Melanitta perspicillata

Trumpeter Swan
Cygnus buccinator

Tundra Swan
Cygnus columbianus

Wood Duck
Aix sponsa

FALCONS AND CARACARAS
PAGE | Order: Falconiformes, Family: Falconidae

American Kestrel
Falco sparverius

Aplomado Falcon
Falco femoralis

Crested Caracara
Caracara cheriway

Gyrfalcon
Falco rusticolus

Merlin
columbarius

Peregrine Falcon
Falco peregrinus

Prairie Falcon
Falco mexicanus

FINCHES, EUPHONIAS, AND ALLIES (1)
PAGE | Order: Passeriformes, Family: Fringillidae

Akekee
Loxops caeruleirostris

Akiapolaau
Hemignathus wilsoni

Akikiki
Oreomystis bairdi

Akohekohe
Palmeria dolei

American Goldfinch
Spinus tristis

Anianiau
Magumma parva

Apapane
Himatione sanguinea

Black Mamo
Drepanis funerea

Black Rosy-Finch
Leucosticte atrata

Brown-capped Rosy-Finch
Leucosticte australis

Cassia Crossbill
Loxia sinesciuris

Cassin's Finch
Haemorhous cassinii

Common Redpoll
Acanthis flammea

Evening Grosbeak
Coccothraustes vespertinus

Gray-crowned Rosy-Finch
Leucosticte tephrocotis

Greater Amakihi
Viridonia sagittirostris

Greater Koa-Finch
Rhodacanthis palmeri

Hawaii Akepa
Loxops coccineus

Hawaii Amakihi
Chlorodrepanis virens

Hawaii Creeper
Loxops mana

Hawaii Mamo
Drepanis pacifica

Hoary Redpoll
Acanthis hornemanni

House Finch
Haemorhous mexicanus

Iiwi
Drepanis coccinea

Kakawahie
Paroreomyza flammea

FINCHES, EUPHONIAS, AND ALLIES (2)
Order: Passeriformes, Family: Fringillidae

Kauai Akialoa
Akialoa stejnegeri

Kauai Amakihi
Chlorodrepanis stejnegeri

Kauai Nukupuu
Hemignathus hanapepe

Kona Grosbeak
Chloridops kona

Lanai Hookbill
Dysmorodrepanis munroi

Lawrence's Goldfinch
Spinus lawrencei

Laysan Finch
Telespiza cantans

Lesser Akialoa
Akialoa obscura

Lesser Goldfinch
Spinus psaltria

Lesser Koa-Finch
Rhodacanthis flaviceps

Maui Akepa
Loxops ochraceus

Maui Alauahio
Paroreomyza montana

Maui Nukupuu
Hemignathus affinis

Maui Parrotbill
Pseudonestor xanthophrys

Maui-nui Akialoa
Akialoa lanaiensis

Nihoa Finch
Telespiza ultima

Oahu Akepa
Loxops wolstenholmei

Oahu Akialoa
Akialoa ellisiana

Oahu Alauahio
Paroreomyza maculata

Oahu Amakihi
Chlorodrepanis flava

Oahu Nukupuu
Hemignathus lucidus

Ou
Psittirostra psittacea

Palila
Loxioides bailleui

Pine Grosbeak
Pinicola enucleator

Pine Siskin
Spinus pinus

Poo-uli
Melamprosops phaeosoma

Purple Finch
Haemorhous purpureus

Red Crossbill
Loxia curvirostra

Ula-ai-hawane
Ciridops anna

White-winged Crossbill
Loxia leucoptera

FRIGATEBIRDS
Order: Suliformes, Family: Fregatidae

Great Frigatebird
Fregata minor

Magnificent Frigatebird
Fregata magnificens

GNATCATCHERS
Order: Passeriformes, Family: Polioptilidae

Black-tailed Gnatcatcher
Polioptila melanura

Blue-gray Gnatcatcher
Polioptila caerulea

California Gnatcatcher
Polioptila californica

GREBES
Order: Podicipediformes, Family: Podicipedidae

Clark's Grebe
Aechmophorus clarkii

Eared Grebe
Podiceps nigricollis

Horned Grebe
Podiceps auritus

Least Grebe
Tachybaptus dominicus

Pied-billed Grebe
Podilymbus podiceps

Red-necked Grebe
Podiceps grisegena

Western Grebe
Aechmophorus occidentalis

GUANS, CHACHALACAS, CURASSOWS
Order: Galliformes, Family: Cracidae

Plain Chachalaca
Ortalis vetula

GULLS, TERNS, AND SKIMMERS (1)
Order: Charadriiformes, Family: Laridae

Aleutian Tern
Onychoprion aleuticus

Arctic Tern
Sterna paradisaea

Black Skimmer
Rynchops niger

Black Tern
Chlidonias niger

Black-legged Kittiwake
Rissa tridactyla

Bonaparte's Gull
Chroicocephalus philadelphia

Bridled Tern
Onychoprion anaethetus

Brown Noddy
Anous stolidus

California Gull
Larus californicus

Caspian Tern
Hydroprogne caspia

GULLS, TERNS, AND SKIMMERS (2)
Order: Charadriiformes, Family: Laridae

Common Tern
Sterna hirundo

Elegant Tern
Thalasseus elegans

Forster's Tern
Sterna forsteri

Franklin's Gull
Leucophaeus pipixcan

Glaucous Gull
Larus hyperboreus

Glaucous-winged Gull
Larus glaucescens

Gray-backed Tern
Onychoprion lunatus

Great Black-backed
Gull *Larus marinus*

Gull-billed Tern
Gelochelidon nilotica

Heermann's Gull
Larus heermanni

Herring Gull
Larus argentatus

Iceland Gull
Larus glaucoides

Ivory Gull
Pagophila eburnea

Laughing Gull
Leucophaeus atricilla

Least Tern
Sternula antillarum

Little Gull
Hydrocoloeus minutus

Mew Gull
Larus canus

Red-legged Kittiwake
Rissa brevirostris

Ring-billed Gull
Larus delawarensis

Roseate Tern
Sterna dougallii

Royal Tern
Thalasseus maximus

Sabine's Gull
Xema sabini

Sandwich Tern
Thalasseus sandvicensis

Sooty Tern
Onychoprion fuscatus

Western Gull
Larus occidentalis

White Tern
Gygis alba

Yellow-footed Gull
Larus livens

HAWAIIAN HONEYEATERS
Order: Passeriformes, Family: Mohoidae

Bishop's Oo
Moho bishopi

Hawaii Oo
Moho nobilis

Kauai Oo
Moho braccatus

Kioea
Chaetoptila angustipluma

Oahu Oo
Moho apicalis

HAWKS, EAGLES, AND KITES
PAGE | Order: Accipitriformes, Family: Accipitridae

Bald Eagle
Haliaeetus leucocephalus

Broad-winged Hawk
Buteo platypterus

Common Black Hawk
Buteogallus anthracinus

Cooper's Hawk
Accipiter cooperii

Ferruginous Hawk
Buteo regalis

Golden Eagle
Aquila chrysaetos

Gray Hawk
Buteo plagiatus

Harris's Hawk
Parabuteo unicinctus

Hawaiian Hawk
Buteo solitarius

Mississippi Kite
Ictinia mississippiensis

Northern Goshawk
Accipiter gentilis

Red-shouldered Hawk
Buteo lineatus

Red-tailed Hawk
Buteo jamaicensis

Rough-legged Hawk
Buteo lagopus

Sharp-shinned Hawk
Accipiter striatus

Short-tailed Hawk
Buteo brachyurus

Snail Kite
Rostrhamus sociabilis

Swainson's Hawk
Buteo swainsoni

Swallow-tailed Kite
Elanoides forficatus

White-tailed Hawk
Geranoaetus albicaudatus

White-tailed Kite
Elanus leucurus

Zone-tailed Hawk
Buteo albonotatus

HERONS, EGRETS, AND BITTERNS (1)
PAGE | Order: Pelecaniformes, Family: Ardeidae

American Bittern
Botaurus lentiginosus

Black-crowned Night-Heron
Nycticorax nycticorax

Cattle Egret
Bubulcus ibis

Great Blue Heron
Ardea herodias

Great Egret
Ardea alba

Green Heron
Butorides virescens

Least Bittern
Ixobrychus exilis

Little Blue Heron
Egretta caerulea

Reddish Egret
Egretta rufescens

Snowy Egret
Egretta thula

HERONS, EGRETS, AND BITTERNS (2)
PAGE | Order: Pelecaniformes, Family: Ardeidae

Tricolored Heron
Egretta tricolor

Yellow-crowned Night-Heron
Nyctanassa violacea

HUMMINGBIRDS
PAGE | Order: Caprimulgiformes, Family: Trochilidae

Allen's Hummingbird
Selasphorus sasin

Anna's Hummingbird
Calypte anna

Black-chinned Hummingbird
Archilochus alexandri

Blue-throated Hummingbird
Lampornis clemenciae

Broad-billed Hummingbird
Cynanthus latirostris

Broad-tailed Hummingbird
Selasphorus platycercus

Buff-bellied Hummingbird
Selasphorus calliope

Calliope Hummingbird
Aythya affinis

Costa's Hummingbird
Calypte costae

Lucifer Hummingbird
Calothorax lucifer

Rivoli's Hummingbird
Eugenes fulgens

Ruby-throated Hummingbird
Archilochus colubris

Rufous Hummingbird
Selasphorus rufus

Violet-crowned Hummingbird
Amazilia violiceps

Xantus's Hummingbird
Hylocharis xantusii

Ibises and Spoonbills
PAGE | Order: Pelecaniformes, Family: Threskiornithidae

Glossy Ibis
Plegadis falcinellus

Roseate Spoonbill
Platalea ajaja

White Ibis
Eudocimus albus

White-faced Ibis
Plegadis chihi

Jacanas
PAGE | Order: Charadriiformes, Family: Jacanidae

Northern Jacana
Jacana spinosa

KINGFISHERS
PAGE | Order: Coraciiformes, Family: Alcedinidae

Belted Kingfisher
Megaceryle alcyon

Green Kingfisher
Chloroceryle americana

Ringed Kingfisher
Megaceryle torquata

KINGLETS
PAGE | Order: Passeriformes, Family: Regulidae

Golden-crowned Kinglet
Regulus satrapa

Ruby-crowned Kinglet
Regulus calendula

LARKS
PAGE | Order: Passeriformes, Family: Alaudidae

Eurasian Skylark
Alauda arvensis

Horned Lark
Eremophila alpestris

LAUGHINGTHRUSHES AND ALLIES
PAGE | Order: Passeriformes, Family: Leiothrichidae

Red-billed Leiothrix
Leiothrix lutea

LEAF WARBLERS
PAGE | Order: Passeriformes, Family: Phylloscopidae

Arctic Warbler
Phylloscopus borealis

LIMPKIN
PAGE | Order: Gruiformes, Family: Aramidae

Limpkin
Aramus guarauna

LONG-TAILED TITS
PAGE | Order: Passeriformes, Family: Aegithalidae

Bushtit
Psaltriparus minimus

LONGSPURS AND SNOW BUNTINGS
PAGE | Order: Passeriformes, Family: Calcariidae

- Chestnut-collared Longspur
  Calcarius ornatus
- Lapland Longspur
  Calcarius lapponicus
- McCown's Longspur
  Rhynchophanes mccownii
- McKay's Bunting
  Plectrophenax hyperboreus
- Smith's Longspur
  Calcarius pictus
- Snow Bunting
  Plectrophenax nivalis

LOONS
PAGE | Order: Gaviiformes, Family: Gaviidae

- Arctic Loon
  Gavia arctica
- Common Loon
  Gavia immer
- Pacific Loon
  Gavia pacifica
- Red-throated Loon
  Gavia stellata
- Yellow-billed Loon
  Gavia adamsii

MOCKINGBIRDS AND THRASHERS
PAGE | Order: Passeriformes, Family: Mimidae

- Bendire's Thrasher
  Toxostoma bendirei
- Brown Thrasher
  Toxostoma rufum
- California Thrasher
  Toxostoma redivivum
- Crissal Thrasher
  Toxostoma crissale
- Curve-billed Thrasher
  Toxostoma curvirostre
- Gray Catbird
  Dumetella carolinensis
- LeConte's Thrasher
  Toxostoma lecontei
- Long-billed Thrasher
  Toxostoma longirostre
- Northern Mockingbird
  Mimus polyglottos
- Sage Thrasher
  Oreoscoptes montanus

MONARCH FLYCATCHERS
PAGE | Order: Passeriformes, Family: Monarchidae

- Hawaii Elepaio
  Chasiempis sandwichensis
- Kauai Elepaio
  Chasiempis sclateri
- Oahu Elepaio
  Chasiempis ibidis

NEW WORLD QUAIL
PAGE | Order: Galliformes, Family: Odontophoridae

- California Quail
  Callipepla californica
- Gambel's Quail
  Callipepla gambelii
- Montezuma Quail
  Cyrtonyx montezumae
- Mountain Quail
  Oreortyx pictus
- Northern Bobwhite
  Colinus virginianus
- Scaled Quail
  Callipepla squamata

NEW WORLD SPARROWS (1)
PAGE | Order: Passeriformes, Family: Passerellidae

- Abert's Towhee
  Melozone aberti
- American Tree Sparrow
  Spizelloides arborea
- Bachman's Sparrow
  Peucaea aestivalis
- Baird's Sparrow
  Centronyx bairdii
- Bell's Sparrow
  Artemisiospiza belli
- Black-chinned Sparrow
  Spizella atrogularis
- Black-throated Sparrow
  Amphispiza bilineata
- Botteri's Sparrow
  Peucaea botterii
- Brewer's Sparrow
  Spizella breweri
- California Towhee
  Melozone fusca
- Canyon Towhee
  Melozone fusca
- Cassin's Sparrow
  Peucaea cassinii
- Chipping Sparrow
  Spizella passerina
- Clay-colored Sparrow
  Spizella pallida
- Dark-eyed Junco
  Junco hyemalis
- Eastern Towhee
  Pipilo erythrophthalmus
- Field Sparrow
  Spizella pusilla
- Five-striped Sparrow
  Amphispiza quinquestriata
- Fox Sparrow
  Passerella iliaca
- Golden-crowned Sparrow
  Zonotrichia atricapilla
- Grasshopper Sparrow
  Ammodramus savannarum
- Green-tailed Towhee
  Pipilo chlorurus
- Harris's Sparrow
  Zonotrichia querula
- Henslow's Sparrow
  Centronyx henslowii
- Lark Bunting
  Calamospiza melanocorys
- Lark Sparrow
  Chondestes grammacus
- LeConte's Sparrow
  Ammospiza leconteii

NEW WORLD SPARROWS (2)
PAGE | Order: Passeriformes, Family: Passerellidae

- Lincoln's Sparrow
  Melospiza lincolnii
- Nelson's Sparrow
  Ammospiza nelsoni
- Olive Sparrow
  Arremonops rufivirgatus
- Rufous-crowned Sparrow
  Aimophila ruficeps
- Rufous-winged Sparrow
  Peucaea carpalis
- Sagebrush Sparrow
  Artemisiospiza nevadensis
- Saltmarsh Sparrow
  Ammospiza caudacuta
- Savannah Sparrow
  Passerculus sandwichensis
- Seaside Sparrow
  Ammospiza maritima
- Song Sparrow
  Melospiza melodia
- Spotted Towhee
  Pipilo maculatus
- Swamp Sparrow
  Melospiza georgiana
- Vesper Sparrow
  Pooecetes gramineus
- White-crowned Sparrow
  Zonotrichia leucophrys
- White-throated Sparrow
  Zonotrichia albicollis
- Yellow-eyed Junco
  Junco phaeonotus

NEW WORLD VULTURES
PAGE | Order: Cathartiformes, Family: Cathartidae

- Black Vulture
  Coragyps atratus
- California Condor
  Gymnogyps californianus
- Turkey Vulture
  Cathartes aura

NEW WORLD WARBLERS (1)
PAGE | Order: Passeriformes, Family: Parulidae

- American Redstart
  Setophaga ruticilla
- Bachman's Warbler
  Vermivora bachmanii
- Bay-breasted Warbler
  Setophaga castanea
- Black-and-white Warbler
  Mniotilta varia
- Black-throated Blue Warbler
  Setophaga caerulescens
- Black-throated Gray Warbler
  Setophaga nigrescens
- Black-throated Green Warbler
  Setophaga virens
- Blackburnian Warbler
  Setophaga fusca
- Blackpoll Warbler
  Setophaga striata
- Blue-winged Warbler
  Vermivora cyanoptera

NEW WORLD WARBLERS (2)
PAGE Order: Passeriformes, Family: Parulidae

Canada Warbler
Cardellina canadensis

Cape May Warbler
Setophaga tigrina

Cerulean Warbler
Setophaga cerulea

Chestnut-sided Warbler
Setophaga pensylvanica

Colima Warbler
Oreothlypis crissalis

Common Yellowthroat
Geothlypis trichas

Connecticut Warbler
Oporornis agilis

Golden-cheeked Warbler
Setophaga chrysoparia

Golden-winged Warbler
Vermivora chrysoptera

Grace's Warbler
Setophaga graciae

Hermit Warbler
Setophaga occidentalis

Hooded Warbler
Setophaga citrina

Kentucky Warbler
Geothlypis formosa

Kirtland's Warbler
Setophaga kirtlandii

Louisiana Waterthrush
Parkesia motacilla

Lucy's Warbler
Oreothlypis luciae

MacGillivray's Warbler
Geothlypis tolmiei

Magnolia Warbler
Setophaga magnolia

Mourning Warbler
Geothlypis philadelphia

Nashville Warbler
Oreothlypis ruficapilla

Northern Parula
Setophaga americana

Northern Waterthrush
Parkesia noveboracensis

Orange-crowned Warbler
Oreothlypis celata

Ovenbird
Seiurus aurocapilla

Painted Redstart
Myioborus pictus

Palm Warbler
Setophaga palmarum

Pine Warbler
Setophaga pinus

Prairie Warbler
Setophaga discolor

Prothonotary Warbler
Protonotaria citrea

Red-faced Warbler
Cardellina rubrifrons

Swainson's Warbler
Limnothlypis swainsonii

Tennessee Warbler
Oreothlypis peregrina

Townsend's Warbler
Setophaga townsendi

Tropical Parula
Setophaga pitiayumi

Virginia's Warbler
Oreothlypis virginiae

NEW WORLD WARBLERS (3)
PAGE Order: Passeriformes, Family: Parulidae

Wilson's Warbler
Cardellina pusilla

Worm-eating Warbler
Helmitheros vermivorum

Yellow Warbler
Setophaga petechia

Yellow-rumped Warbler
Setophaga coronata

Yellow-throated Warbler
Setophaga dominica

NEW WORLD AND AFRICAN PARROTS
PAGE Order: Psittaciformes, Family: Psittacidae

Carolina Parakeet
Conuropsis carolinensis

Monk Parakeet
Myiopsitta monachus

Red-crowned Parrot
Amazona viridigenalis

Thick-billed Parrot
Rhynchopsitta pachyrhyncha

White-winged Parakeet
Brotogeris versicolurus

Yellow-chevroned Parakeet
Brotogeris chiriri

NIGHTJARS AND ALLIES
PAGE Order: Caprimulgiformes, Family: Caprimulgidae

Antillean Nighthawk
Chordeiles gundlachii

Buff-collared Nightjar
Antrostomus ridgwayi

Chuck-will's-widow
Antrostomus carolinensis

Common Nighthawk
Chordeiles minor

Common Pauraque
Nyctidromus albicollis

Common Poorwill
Phalaenoptilus nuttallii

Eastern Whip-poor-will
Antrostomus vociferus

Lesser Nighthawk
Chordeiles acutipennis

Mexican Whip-poor-will
Antrostomus arizonae

Common Poorwill
Phalaenoptilus nuttallii

NORTHERN STORM-PETRELS
PAGE Order: Procellariiformes, Family: Hydrobatidae

Ashy Storm-Petrel
Oceanodroma homochroa

Band-rumped Storm-Petrel
Oceanodroma castro

Black Storm-Petrel
Oceanodroma melania

Fork-tailed Storm-Petrel
Oceanodroma furcata

Leach's Storm-Petrel
Oceanodroma leucorhoa

Tristram's Storm-Petrel
Oceanodroma tristrami

NUTHATCHES
PAGE Order: Passeriformes, Family: Sittidae

Brown-headed Nuthatch
Sitta pusilla

Pygmy Nuthatch
Sitta pygmaea

Red-breasted Nuthatch
Sitta canadensis

White-breasted Nuthatch
Sitta carolinensis

OLD WORLD FLYCATCHERS
PAGE Order: Passeriformes, Family: Muscicapidae

Bluethroat
Luscinia svecica

Northern Wheatear
Oenanthe oenanthe

White-rumped Shama
Copsychus malabaricus

OLD WORLD SPARROWS
PAGE Order: Passeriformes, Family: Passeridae

Eurasian Tree Sparrow
Passer montanus

House Sparrow
Passer domesticus

OLIVE WARBLER
PAGE Order: Passeriformes, Family: Peucedramidae

Olive Warbler
Peucedramus taeniatus

OSPREY
PAGE Order: Accipitriformes, Family: Pandionidae

Osprey
Pandion haliaetus

OWLS (1)
PAGE Order: Strigiformes, Family: Strigidae

Barred Owl
Strix varia

Boreal Owl
Aegolius funereus

Burrowing Owl
Athene cunicularia

Eastern Screech-Owl
Megascops asio

Elf Owl
Micrathene whitneyi

Ferruginous Pygmy-Owl
Glaucidium brasilianum

Flammulated Owl
Psiloscops flammeolus

Great Gray Owl
Strix nebulosa

OWLS (2)
PAGE | Order: Strigiformes, Family: Strigidae

Great Horned Owl
Bubo virginianus

Long-eared Owl
Asio otus

Northern Hawk Owl
Surnia ulula

Northern Pygmy-Owl
Glaucidium gnoma

Northern Saw-whet Owl
Aegolius acadicus

Short-eared Owl
Asio flammeus

Snowy Owl
Bubo scandiacus

Spotted Owl
Strix occidentalis

Western Screech-Owl
Megascops kennicottii

Whiskered Screech-Owl
Megascops trichopsis

OYSTERCATCHERS
PAGE | Order: Charadriiformes, Family: Haematopodidae

American Oystercatcher
Haematopus palliatus

Black Oystercatcher
Haematopus bachmani

PARROTBILLS, WRENTIT, AND ALLIES
PAGE | Order: Passeriformes, Family: Paradoxornithidae

Wrentit
Chamaea fasciata

PELICANS
PAGE | Order: Pelecaniformes, Family: Pelecanidae

American White Pelican
Pelecanus erythrorhynchos

Brown Pelican
Pelecanus occidentalis

PENDULINE-TITS
PAGE | Order: Passeriformes, Family: Remizidae

Verdin
Auriparus flaviceps

PHEASANTS, GROUSE, AND ALLIES (1)
PAGE | Order: Galliformes, Family: Phasianidae

Black Francolin
Francolinus francolinus

Chukar
Alectoris chukar

Dusky Grouse
Dendragapus obscurus

Erckel's Francolin
Pternistis erckelii

PHEASANTS, GROUSE, AND ALLIES (2)
PAGE | Order: Galliformes, Family: Phasianidae

Gray Francolin
Francolinus pondicerianus

Gray Partridge
Perdix perdix

Greater Prairie-Chicken
Tympanuchus cupido

Greater Sage-Grouse
Centrocercus urophasianus

Gunnison Sage-Grouse
Centrocercus minimus

Himalayan Snowcock
Tetraogallus himalayensis

Indian Peafowl
Pavo cristatus

Lesser Prairie-Chicken
Tympanuchus pallidicinctus

Ring-necked Pheasant
Phasianus colchicus

Rock Ptarmigan
Lagopus muta

Ruffed Grouse
Bonasa umbellus

Sharp-tailed Grouse
Tympanuchus phasianellus

Sooty Grouse
Dendragapus fuliginosus

Spruce Grouse
Falcipennis canadensis

White-tailed Ptarmigan
Lagopus leucura

Wild Turkey
Meleagris gallopavo

Willow Ptarmigan
Lagopus lagopus

PIGEONS AND DOVES
PAGE | Order: Columbiformes, Family: Columbidae

Band-tailed Pigeon
Patagioenas fasciata

Common Ground-Dove
Columbina passerina

Eurasian Collared-Dove
Streptopelia decaocto

Inca Dove
Columbina inca

Mourning Dove
Zenaida macroura

Passenger Pigeon
Ectopistes migratorius

Red-billed Pigeon
Patagioenas flavirostris

Rock Pigeon
Columba livia

Spotted Dove
Streptopelia chinensis

White-crowned Pigeon
Patagioenas leucocephala

White-tipped Dove
Leptotila verreauxi

White-winged Dove
Zenaida asiatica

PLOVERS AND LAPWINGS
PAGE | Order: Charadriiformes, Family: Charadriidae

American Golden-Plover
Pluvialis dominica

Black-bellied Plover
Pluvialis squatarola

Killdeer
Charadrius vociferus

Mountain Plover
Charadrius montanus

Pacific Golden-Plover
Pluvialis fulva

Piping Plover
Charadrius melodus

Semipalmated Plover
Charadrius semipalmatus

Snowy Plover
Charadrius nivosus

Wilson's Plover
Charadrius wilsonia

RAILS, GALLINULES, AND COOTS
PAGE | Order: Gruiformes, Family: Rallidae

American Coot
Fulica americana

Black Rail
Laterallus jamaicensis

Clapper Rail
Rallus crepitans

Common Gallinule
Gallinula galeata

Gray-headed Swamphen
Porphyrio poliocephalus

Hawaiian Coot
Fulica alai

Hawaiian Rail
Zapornia sandwichensis

King Rail
Rallus elegans

Laysan Rail
Zapornia palmeri

Purple Gallinule
Porphyrio martinica

Ridgway's Rail
Rallus obsoletus

Sora
Porzana carolina

Virginia Rail
Rallus limicola

Yellow Rail
Coturnicops noveboracensis

REED WARBLERS AND ALLIES
PAGE | Order: Passeriformes, Family: Acrocephalidae

Millerbird
Acrocephalus familiaris

SANDPIPERS AND ALLIES (1)
PAGE   Order: Charadriiformes, Family: Scolopacidae

American Woodcock
Scolopax minor

Baird's Sandpiper
Calidris bairdii

Bar-tailed Godwit
Limosa lapponica

Black Turnstone
Arenaria melanocephala

Bristle-thighed Curlew
Numenius tahitiensis

Buff-breasted Sandpiper
Calidris subruficollis

Dunlin
Calidris alpina

Eskimo Curlew
Numenius borealis

Greater Yellowlegs
Tringa melanoleuca

Hudsonian Godwit
Limosa haemastica

Least Sandpiper
Calidris minutilla

Lesser Yellowlegs
Tringa flavipes

Long-billed Curlew
Numenius americanus

Long-billed Dowitcher
Limnodromus scolopaceus

Marbled Godwit
Limosa fedoa

Pectoral Sandpiper
Calidris melanotos

Purple Sandpiper
Calidris maritima

Red Knot
Calidris canutus

Red Phalarope
Phalaropus fulicarius

Red-necked Phalarope
Phalaropus lobatus

Rock Sandpiper
Calidris ptilocnemis

Ruddy Turnstone
Arenaria interpres

Sanderling
Calidris alba

Semipalmated Sandpiper
Calidris pusilla

Short-billed Dowitcher
Limnodromus griseus

Solitary Sandpiper
Tringa solitaria

Spotted Sandpiper
Actitis macularius

Stilt Sandpiper
Calidris himantopus

Surfbird
Calidris virgata

Upland Sandpiper
Bartramia longicauda

Wandering Tattler
Tringa incana

Western Sandpiper
Calidris mauri

Whimbrel
Numenius phaeopus

White-rumped Sandpiper
Calidris fuscicollis

Willet
Tringa semipalmata

SANDPIPERS AND ALLIES (2)
PAGE   Order: Charadriiformes, Family: Scolopacidae

Wilson's Phalarope
Phalaropus tricolor

Wilson's Snipe
Gallinago delicata

SHEARWATERS AND PETRELS
PAGE   Order: Procellariiformes, Family: Procellariidae

Black-vented Shearwater
Puffinus opisthomelas

Bonin Petrel
Pterodroma hypoleuca

Bulwer's Petrel
Bulweria bulwerii

Christmas Shearwater
Puffinus nativitatis

Hawaiian Petrel
Pterodroma sandwichensis

Manx Shearwater
Puffinus puffinus

Newell's Shearwater
Puffinus newelli

Northern Fulmar
Fulmarus glacialis

Townsend's Shearwater
Puffinus auricularis

Wedge-tailed Shearwater
Ardenna pacifica

SHRIKES
PAGE   Order: Passeriformes, Family: Laniidae

Loggerhead Shrike
Lanius ludovicianus

Northern Shrike
Lanius borealis

SILKY-FLYCATCHERS
PAGE   Order: Passeriformes, Family: Ptiliogonatidae

Phainopepla
Phainopepla nitens

SKUAS AND JAEGERS
PAGE   Order: Charadriiformes, Family: Stercorariidae

Long-tailed Jaeger
Stercorarius longicaudus

Parasitic Jaeger
Stercorarius parasiticus

Pomarine Jaeger
Stercorarius pomarinus

STARLINGS
PAGE   Order: Passeriformes, Family: Sturnidae

Common Myna
Acridotheres tristis

Crested Myna
Acridotheres cristatellus

European Starling
Sturnus vulgaris

STILTS AND AVOCETS
PAGE   Order: Charadriiformes, Family: Recurvirostridae

American Avocet
Recurvirostra americana

Black-necked Stilt
Himantopus mexicanus

STORKS
PAGE   Order: Ciconiiformes, Family: Ciconiidae

Wood Stork
Mycteria americana

SWALLOWS
PAGE   Order: Passeriformes, Family: Hirundinidae

Bank Swallow
Riparia riparia

Barn Swallow
Hirundo rustica

Cave Swallow
Petrochelidon fulva

Cliff Swallow
Petrochelidon pyrrhonota

Northern Rough-winged Swallow
Stelgidopteryx serripennis

Purple Martin
Progne subis

Tree Swallow
Tachycineta bicolor

Violet-green Swallow
Tachycineta thalassina

SWIFTS
PAGE   Order: Caprimulgiformes, Family: Apodidae

Black Swift
Cypseloides niger

Chimney Swift
Chaetura pelagica

Vaux's Swift
Chaetura vauxi

White-throated Swift
Aeronautes saxatalis

TANAGERS AND ALLIES
PAGE   Order: Passeriformes, Family: Thraupidae

Morelet's Seedeater
Sporophila morelleti

THRUSHES AND ALLIES
PAGE | Order: Passeriformes, Family: Turdidae

- Amaui
  Myadestes woahensis
- American Robin
  Turdus migratorius
- Bicknell's Thrush
  Catharus bicknelli
- Eastern Bluebird
  Sialia sialis
- Gray-cheeked Thrush
  Catharus minimus
- Hermit Thrush
  Catharus guttatus
- Kamao
  Myadestes myadestinus
- Mountain Bluebird
  Sialia currucoides
- Olomao
  Myadestes lanaiensis
- Omao
  Myadestes obscurus
- Puaiohi
  Myadestes palmeri
- Swainson's Thrush
  Catharus ustulatus
- Townsend's Solitaire
  Myadestes townsendi
- Varied Thrush
  Ixoreus naevius
- Veery
  Catharus fuscescens
- Western Bluebird
  Sialia mexicana
- Wood Thrush
  Hylocichla mustelina

TITS, CHICKADEES, AND TITMICE
PAGE | Order: Passeriformes, Family: Paridae

- Black-capped Chickadee
  Poecile atricapillus
- Black-crested Titmouse
  Baeolophus atricristatus
- Boreal Chickadee
  Poecile hudsonicus
- Bridled Titmouse
  Baeolophus wollweberi
- Carolina Chickadee
  Poecile carolinensis
- Chestnut-backed Chickadee
  Poecile rufescens
- Gray-headed Chickadee
  Poecile cinctus
- Juniper Titmouse
  Baeolophus ridgwayi
- Mexican Chickadee
  Poecile sclateri
- Mountain Chickadee
  Poecile gambeli
- Oak Titmouse
  Baeolophus inornatus
- Tufted Titmouse
  Baeolophus bicolor

TREECREEPERS
PAGE | Order: Passeriformes, Family: Certhiidae

- Brown Creeper
  Certhia americana

TROGONS
PAGE | Order: Trogoniformes, Family: Trogonidae

- Elegant Trogon
  Trogon elegans

TROPICBIRDS
PAGE | Order: Phaethontiformes, Family: Phaethontidae

- Red-tailed Tropicbird
  Phaethon rubricauda
- White-tailed Tropicbird
  Phaethon lepturus
- Pacific Golden-Plover
  Pluvialis fulva

TROUPIALS AND ALLIES
PAGE | Order: Passeriformes, Family: Icteridae

- Altamira Oriole
  Icterus gularis
- Audubon's Oriole
  Icterus graduacauda
- Baltimore Oriole
  Icterus galbula
- Boat-tailed Grackle
  Quiscalus major
- Bobolink
  Dolichonyx oryzivorus
- Brewer's Blackbird
  Euphagus cyanocephalus
- Bronzed Cowbird
  Molothrus aeneus
- Brown-headed Cowbird
  Molothrus ater
- Bullock's Oriole
  Icterus bullockii
- Common Grackle
  Quiscalus quiscula
- Eastern Meadowlark
  Sturnella magna
- Great-tailed Grackle
  Quiscalus mexicanus
- Hooded Oriole
  Icterus cucullatus
- Orchard Oriole
  Icterus spurius
- Red-winged Blackbird
  Agelaius phoeniceus
- Rusty Blackbird
  Euphagus carolinus
- Scott's Oriole
  Icterus parisorum
- Shiny Cowbird
  Molothrus bonariensis
- Tricolored Blackbird
  Agelaius tricolor
- Western Meadowlark
  Sturnella neglecta
- Yellow-headed Blackbird
  Xanthocephalus xanthocephalus

TYRANT FLYCATCHERS
PAGE | Order: Passeriformes, Family: Tyrannidae

- Acadian Flycatcher
  Empidonax virescens
- Alder Flycatcher
  Empidonax alnorum
- Ash-throated Flycatcher
  Myiarchus cinerascens
- Black Phoebe
  Sayornis nigricans
- Brown-crested Flycatcher
  Myiarchus tyrannulus
- Buff-breasted Flycatcher
  Empidonax fulvifrons
- Cassin's Kingbird
  Tyrannus vociferans
- Cordilleran Flycatcher
  Empidonax occidentalis
- Couch's Kingbird
  Tyrannus couchii
- Dusky Flycatcher
  Empidonax oberholseri
- Dusky-capped Flycatcher
  Myiarchus tuberculifer
- Eastern Kingbird
  Tyrannus tyrannus
- Eastern Phoebe
  Sayornis phoebe
- Eastern Wood-Pewee
  Contopus virens
- Gray Flycatcher
  Empidonax wrightii
- Gray Kingbird
  Tyrannus dominicensis
- Great Crested Flycatcher
  Myiarchus crinitus
- Great Kiskadee
  Pitangus sulphuratus
- Greater Pewee
  Contopus pertinax
- Hammond's Flycatcher
  Empidonax hammondii
- Least Flycatcher
  Empidonax minimus
- Olive-sided Flycatcher
  Contopus cooperi
- Pacific-slope Flycatcher
  Empidonax difficilis
- Say's Phoebe
  Sayornis saya
- Scissor-tailed Flycatcher
  Tyrannus forficatus
- Sulphur-bellied Flycatcher
  Myiodynastes luteiventris
- Thick-billed Kingbird
  Tyrannus crassirostris
- Tropical Kingbird
  Tyrannus melancholicus
- Vermilion Flycatcher
  Pyrocephalus rubinus
- Western Kingbird
  Tyrannus verticalis
- Western Wood-Pewee
  Contopus sordidulus
- Willow Flycatcher
  Empidonax traillii
- Yellow-bellied Flycatcher
  Empidonax flaviventris
- Vermilion Flycatcher
  Pyrocephalus rubinus
- Vermilion Flycatcher
  Pyrocephalus rubinus

VIREOS, SHRIKE-BABBLERS, ERPORNIS
PAGE | Order: Passeriformes, Family: Vireonidae

Bell's Vireo
Vireo bellii

Black-capped Vireo
Vireo atricapilla

Black-whiskered Vireo
Vireo altiloquus

Blue-headed Vireo
Vireo solitarius

Cassin's Vireo
Vireo cassinii

Gray Vireo
Vireo vicinior

Hutton's Vireo
Vireo huttoni

Philadelphia Vireo
Vireo philadelphicus

Plumbeous Vireo
Vireo plumbeus

Warbling Vireo
Vireo gilvus

White-eyed Vireo
Vireo griseus

Yellow-throated Vireo
Vireo flavifrons

WAGTAILS AND PIPITS
PAGE | Order: Passeriformes, Family: Motacillidae

American Pipit
Anthus rubescens

Eastern Yellow Wagtail
Motacilla tschutschensis

Sprague's Pipit
Anthus spragueii

White Wagtail
Motacilla alba

WAXBILLS AND ALLIES
PAGE | Order: Passeriformes, Family: Estrildidae

Java Sparrow
Lonchura oryzivora

WAXWINGS
PAGE | Order: Passeriformes, Family: Bombycillidae

Bohemian Waxwing
Bombycilla garrulus

Cedar Waxwing
Bombycilla cedrorum

WHITE-EYES, YUHINAS AND ALLIES
PAGE | Order: Passeriformes, Family: Zosteropidae

Japanese White-eye
Zosterops japonicus

WOODPECKERS
PAGE | Order: Piciformes, Family: Picidae

Acorn Woodpecker
Melanerpes formicivorus

American Three-toed Woodpecker
Picoides dorsalis

Arizona Woodpecker
Dryobates arizonae

Black-backed Woodpecker
Picoides arcticus

Downy Woodpecker
Dryobates pubescens

Gila Woodpecker
Melanerpes uropygialis

Gilded Flicker
Colaptes chrysoides

Golden-fronted Woodpecker
Melanerpes aurifrons

Hairy Woodpecker
Dryobates villosus

Ivory-billed Woodpecker
Campephilus principalis

Ladder-backed Woodpecker
Dryobates scalaris

Lewis's Woodpecker
Melanerpes lewis

Northern Flicker
Colaptes auratus

Nuttall's Woodpecker
Dryobates nuttallii

Pileated Woodpecker
Dryocopus pileatus

Red-bellied Woodpecker
Melanerpes carolinus

Red-breasted Sapsucker
Sphyrapicus ruber

Red-cockaded Woodpecker
Dryobates borealis

Red-headed Woodpecker
Melanerpes erythrocephalus

Red-naped Sapsucker
Sphyrapicus nuchalis

White-headed Woodpecker
Dryobates albolarvatus

Williamson's Sapsucker
Sphyrapicus thyroideus

Yellow-bellied Sapsucker
Sphyrapicus varius

WRENS
PAGE | Order: Passeriformes, Family: Troglodytidae

Bewick's Wren
Thryomanes bewickii

Cactus Wren
Campylorhynchus brunneicapillus

Canyon Wren
Catherpes mexicanus

House Wren
Troglodytes aedon

Marsh Wren
Cistothorus palustris

Pacific Wren
Troglodytes pacificus

Rock Wren
Salpinctes obsoletus

Sedge Wren
Cistothorus platensis

Winter Wren
Troglodytes hiemalis

YELLOW-BREASTED CHAT
PAGE | Order: Passeriformes, Family: Icteriidae

Yellow-breasted Chat
Icteria virens

OTHER BIRDS
PAGE

Order: | Family:

Order: | Family:

Order: | Family:

Order: | Family:

Order: | Family:

Order: | Family:

Order: | Family:

Order: | Family:

Order: | Family:

Order: | Family:

Order: | Family:

Order: | Family:

Order: | Family:

Order: | Family:

Order: | Family:

Order: | Family:

Order: | Family:

Order: | Family:

Order: | Family:

Order: | Family:

Order: | Family:

Order: | Family:

Order: | Family:

Order: | Family:

Order: | Family:

Order: | Family:

Made in the USA
Columbia, SC
19 February 2019